WHAT EVERYONE NEEDS TO KNOW

About Drugs

WHAT EVERYONE NEEDS TO KNOW

About Drugs

BOOKS by U.S.NEWS & WORLD REPORT

Joseph Newman—Directing Editor

A division of U.S.News & World Report, Inc.

WASHINGTON, D.C.

Contents

Acknowledgments

The editors have had the benefit of the knowledge and experience of both professionals and laymen in gathering material for the three distinct parts of this manuscript: "The Facts About Drugs"; "What Young People Say"; and "What the Experts Say."

A special word of recognition is due officials and other members of the National Institute of Mental Health; Bureau of Narcotics and Dangerous Drugs; Bureau of Customs; Narcotic Treatment Agency; Narcotics Addiction Rehabilitation Corps; members of the Committee on the Judiciary of the United States Senate; the Select Committee on Crime of the House of Representatives; The Menninger Foundation; Daytop Village; Odyssey House; Runaway House and Second Genesis. Others who were particularly generous with their time and knowledge include: Dr. Richard H. Blum, Stanford University; Dr. Everett H. Ellinwood, Jr., Duke University; Dr. Dana L. Farnsworth, Harvard University; Dr. Daniel X. Freedman, University of Chicago; Dr. Kenneth Keniston, Yale University; James S. Sweet, Northwestern University and student research-writers, Lucia Newman, Steve Saferin and James D. Thayer.

PART ONE

The Facts About Drugs

CHAPTER ONE

The Drug Scene

It came as little surprise to most Americans when President Richard M. Nixon declared in February 1970, that "drug misuse is a growing national problem" in which "hundreds of thousands of Americans—young and old alike—endanger their health through the inappropriate use of drugs of all kinds." Recently, the rate of increase in drug consumption has been so great that one federal official estimated that the use of *all* drugs will increase a hundredfold in the next ten years. According to a doctor, "they are practically replacing the function of the virtues in striving for a sane and well-ordered life." Americans are now consuming 1.05 billion gallons of alcoholic beverages each year; pharmacy shelves are brimming with tranquilizers and pep-up pills, three-fourths of which were unknown in 1950; and stories of the 12-year-old heroin addict and the 16-year-old marihuana dealer are now commonplace.

Since drugs have been characterized as any "substance that has an effect on the body or mind," the idea of "drug abuse" is worth defining. Dr. Sidney Cohen, of the National Institute of Mental Health, writes that "it is the persistent and usually excessive self-administration of any drug which has resulted in psychological or physical dependence, or which deviates from approved social patterns of the culture." The more serious problem of "addiction" begins when an individual has so "lost the power of self-control with reference to a drug" that the user or society is harmed. Neither state is desirable for the individual or, because he is rarely a hermit, for the rest of us.

In any discussion of the "national drug problem," experts usually point first to alcohol. About forty-four out of every 1,000 adults in this country are alcoholics, and up to one-half of all arrests each year are for "chronic drunkenness." Other statistics indicate that over 50 percent of the annual deaths and injuries from automobile accidents across the nation either involve or result from alcohol. Heavy use is also known to cause permanent brain damage and cirrhosis, which is the sixth leading cause of death among Americans.

The other side of the picture, of course, is that most people use alcohol safely, understand its benefits as a depressant, and have the judgment and experience to avoid its hazards. The same may be said for other socially approved drugs, such as aspirin, coffee and cigarettes: the majority of their users do not get into trouble with them. Where clear dangers of misuse exist, they are restricted by law to adults.

In the 1930s, most of the drugs abused today were unknown to the American public. Well over half of all prescriptions filled were based on aspirin, phenacetin and caffeine which were combined with codeine, quinine or belladonna to treat serious ailments. Since then, the achievements of the "miracle" drugs have been worthy of their name, and killers like pneumonia, influenza, tuberculosis, diptheria, whooping cough and polio have lost their threat. However, the medical laboratories have also succeeded in isolating heroin from the opium poppy; in synthesizing, and therefore enabling mass production of, the "active" ingredients in many natural mind-drugs like marihuana; in inventing LSD-25 and other hallucinogens; and in creating the stimulants and sedatives which are now consumed by the billion across the nation. The sale of all of these to the general public is either illegal or medically restricted, yet the consumption of these has increased so greatly in the past twenty years that their abuse now constitutes the "national drug problem."

It is of little comfort to know that historically the attractions of drugs are not new. One Stanford University research team reports that:

> One finds over the centuries men seeking—and drugs
> offering—health, relief of pain, security, mystical revela-
> tions, eternal life, the approval of the gods, relaxation,
> joy, sexuality, restraint, blunting of the senses, escape,
> ecstasy, stimulation, freedom from fatigue, sleep, fertility,
> the approval of others, clarity of thought, emotional in-
> tensity, self-understanding, self-improvement, p o w e r,
> wealth, degradation, a life philosophy, exploitation of
> others, enjoyment of others, value enhancement, and
> one's own or another's death.*

But for Americans, who have traditionally been self-reliant in
the achievement of these goals, whether laudable or despica-
ble, the rising pattern of drug dependence *is* new.

The most widely abused of all the restricted drugs today
are the stimulants and sedatives. Medically known as the amphetamines (ups) and the barbiturates (downs) they are cher-
ished by housewives as diet pills; by almost a quarter of our
seven million college students as study aids; and by the crew
of at least one national television network as vital to the successful coverage of Apollo moonshots. They are attractive because they can take the individual beyond his natural limita-
tions, then bring him back again. In abuse, the stimulants can
literally send an individual out of his mind, while the sedatives
are a common cause of death, both intentional and accidental.
Usually these compounds are found in brilliantly colored
gelatin-capsule form, and are produced legally by pharmaceutical companies in the United States. Much blame has been
placed on doctors for their widespread availability; others
point to television. Mayor Lindsay of New York City recently
lambasted the industry for showing commercials encouraging
viewers "to relax with a pill; take off weight with a pill . . .
wake up, slow down, be happy, relieve tension with pills—
that is, with drugs."

---

* Dr. Richard H. Blum et al., *Drugs and Society* (I) (San Francisco: Jossey-Bass
Publications, Inc., 1969).

The mass media have also come under heavy fire for their role in popularizing marihuana and the other "psychedelic" or hallucinogenic drugs, by spreading the word in the late sixties about all the "free spirits" risking possible psychological damage and definite jail sentences by using them. Today, estimates of those who have experimented with marihuana in this country range up to 20 million, and the young have taken over the drug as their own. Another three million young people are estimated to have tried LSD-25 or similar compounds, and although their use seems to be decreasing now, as news of their possible side-effects becomes better known, tragic reports of suicide or psychosis (mental illness) attributed to these drugs are still not uncommon.

Among the experts, controversy still rages about just how dangerous these drugs are. Frequently referred to as the "soft" drugs, because they are nonaddictive, the young argue that "their" drugs are no more dangerous than alcohol. Dr. Richard H. Blum of Stanford University, pointing out that no more than 30 percent of LSD users are hospitalized, and that no more than 10 percent are permanently affected by the drug, thinks they may have something. Unlike the workings of alcohol, however, the action of LSD and other powerful hallucinogens on the body, and more specifically, on the brain, is not yet understood. Uncanny happenings, described as mystical experiences, have been reported by researchers and experimenters alike, but until the nature of these drugs is better understood, it is probably wise to keep in mind the statement of William James in his *Varieties of Religious Experience,* as cited by Dr. Sidney Cohen:

> The sway of alcohol over mankind is unquestionably due to its power to stimulate the mystical faculties of human nature usually crushed to earth by the cold facts and dry criticisms of the sober hour.*

And for now, at least, the "high" of the hallucinogenic drugs is still a "toxic psychosis" to doctors.

---

*Dr. Sidney Cohen, M.D. *The Drug Dilemma* (New York: McGraw-Hill Book Company, 1969).

Just another weed, marihuana, unnoticed by thousands of motorists, grows wild along many U.S. highways. Above is a patch near the Kansas City airport.

The third major group of restricted drugs that are contributing to the problem today are the opiates. In the United States, this means heroin. Approximately one out of every 2,000 U.S. citizens is addicted to the drug, or about 200,000 people. It is also estimated that up to one quarter of these are under 21 years of age.

Unlike the other abused drugs, heroin is a true narcotic, which means, among other things, that steadily increasing doses are needed by the user to reproduce his original satisfaction. In addition, the body develops a genuine physical need for the drug, defined as addiction, which must be satisfied. In most cases, the acquisition of heroin fills the addicted user's life to the exclusion of all else. Purchase of the drug is illegal, and since most users are unemployed, criminal channels are required both to obtain the drug and to acquire the means to do so. Over 50 percent of all burglaries in New York City are attributed to addicts, and in Washington, D.C., which has one of the highest crime rates in the nation, 85 percent of *all* crime is attributed to them by police officials. Clearly, the problem is a serious one both for the user and his society, for which there are no easy solutions.

Unlike most of the abused drugs, heroin is not produced in the United States. About 85 percent comes from Turkey; 5 percent from the Far East; and the rest from Middle Eastern and Latin American countries. Virtually all of it is smuggled in. The cost of its sale to society, in terms of stolen goods and other illegal activity (not to mention human lives) is about $1.5 billion annually. Commercially, the domestic trade is controlled by the Mafia, and as Dr. Cohen has stated in *The Drug Dilemma*: "If the organized crime ring could be eliminated, practically all problems with narcotic addiction would disappear. These people are known; it is scandalous that they are permitted to continue to exploit the most miserable person of all—the addict."

The other difficulty in solving the heroin problem lies with the addict, himself. Most, when cured, relapse again as soon as the drug becomes available once more. Most feel that heroin, by obliterating all pain, improves their lives, and that without it, their world is impossible to face. The finding by research scientists that most addicts took heroin for what, to them, were very good reasons, led to one popular theory that drug abuse came as a result of severe frustration or deprivation in the user's economic, social or family background. Today, with heroin sweeping into the schools, businesses and armed forces of the nation, it is becoming clear that people will experiment with the drug simply because it is there.

Many point to the war, racial troubles and other national crises as aggravating the problem, and while this may be true, it is also worthwhile noting that Sweden, which has not been at war in 160 years and which has no interracial problems, is currently witnessing a drug "epidemic" that proportionately rivals our own. Another insight may come from sub-Saharan Africa, where smoking marihuana has long been old hat, although it is illegal in most of these countries. There, officials report, the young are asserting their independence by not smoking marihuana. Their most serious problems are instead caused by the new-found delights of alcohol. An American correspondent reports that Zambia, whose rate of auto accidents is twelve times our own, "is one of a number of African nations that have begun to plead with their citizens to stop drinking and get back to work."

For Americans, however, the real question ahead is how to solve our own problems with rising drug use. In 1969-70, the Justice Department received its first billion-dollar budget to help provide for new postal inspectors to concentrate on narcotics; more narcotics agents; seventy new border patrol inspectors and radio operators; and the addition of 152 officers at the Bureau of Narcotics and Dangerous Drugs. All of this is an attempt to limit the sale and smuggling of the illegal substances both within and from outside the country. Another more than $300 million was budgeted for the National Institute of Mental Health to provide for further research into the medical and psychological questions raised by the drugs and their users. Finally, based on the latest findings of the National Institute of Mental Health—the Defense Department, the Department of Health, Education and Welfare, the Department of Justice, the Department of Labor and the Office of Economic Opportunity have prepared the following suggestions:

- Society should judge adults who misuse liquor or drugs by the same standards it judges young people. A double standard produces a credibility gap.
- Children should not be continually exposed to the idea that the stresses of daily life require chemical relief.
- Factual information about drugs should be stressed rather than attempts to frighten people.
- Respect for all chemicals, especially mind-altering chemicals, should be instilled in people at an early age.
- Efforts to detect all manufacturers and large-scale traffickers of illicit drugs should increase.
- Further research in prevention, education and treatment techniques should be carried out.

To those who argue that the use of drugs, no matter how destructive, should be purely a matter of personal choice, a civil liberty, these agencies respond that: "It is difficult for an individual to do something to himself that has consequences upon himself alone. Inevitably, the act will have an impact on those who are close to him and those who are dependent upon him. To "drop out" via drugs means that the person becomes dependent upon the social structure for a variety of services and supplies. Someone has to pay the bill. And, in order to avoid paying the bill, these groups advise that the individual "learn as many facts as possible about drugs so that he will understand the problem."

In an effort to provide this understanding, the following chapters attempt to explain the various restricted drugs, their potential for abuse, and how both users and scientists view them.

CHAPTER TWO

The Stimulants and Sedatives

More and more Americans are turning to the chemicals contained in pills for relief from the mounting pressures of modern life. To counter depression and fatigue, they pop pep pills; to allay anxiety, they take tranquilizers; to quiet tension, they swallow sedatives.

These "speed up" and "slow down" drugs account for roughly one-third of all pill prescriptions in the United States. An estimated 8 percent of these prescriptions are for diet or pep pills; 25 percent are for tension-relievers and sleeping pills.

Mood-altering drugs, used to treat conditions of excessive anxiety and to counteract chronic fatigue or depression, can be divided into two basic categories—stimulants and sedatives.

The stimulants act to elevate moods and extend the limits of man's endurance by staving off fatigue. Among the most potent of these drugs are the synthetic amphetamines.

Amphetamines are chemical compounds which, when taken internally, kill the desire to eat and sleep. As powerful stimulants of the central nervous system, these drugs act to release norepinephrine. This substance, which usually is stored in nerve endings, concentrates in the higher centers of the brain, thus forcing the heart to beat faster and the body's metabolism to speed up. Food is rapidly converted to chemical energy.

The basic amphetamine compound is known commercially

as Benzedrine. The d-form, dextroamphetamine sulphate, which has identical basic components but a different chemical structure, is sold as Dexedrine. Methamphetamine, marketed as Methedrine, Desoxyn and others, contains additional elements. Both Dexedrine and Methedrine are more powerful stimulants than Benzedrine.

Desbutal, Dexamyl and Preludin are brand names for stimulant-sedative combinations. Many pharmaceutical companies add sedatives such as barbiturates to their amphetamine capsules in order to "smooth" the action of these stimulants. A sedative will take the edge off or reduce the jittery, hypertense feelings amphetamines often produce.

All of these amphetamine compounds can be obtained with a prescription. Most are very inexpensive, costing only about 5 cents for a 5 milligram capsule the size of an aspirin.

These drugs have been in existence for over fifty years. In 1919, a Japanese clinician, Ogata, first prepared the amphetamine which today is known as "speed" among drug experimenters. Chemically it is described as methamphetamine hydrochloride. The other amphetamine compounds, notably the basic drug marketed as Benzedrine, were produced in 1927 solely to be used as decongestants in the treatment of bronchial asthma and severe colds.

Relatively little use was found for methamphetamine until the 1930s when German clinical researchers found that it possessed stimulant properties similar to those of the other amphetamines. As a result, the German and Japanese armies used it to counteract fatigue and improve combat performance during World War II.

The first widespread misuse of methamphetamine began after World War II, when Japan released its war surplus of this stimulant to the open market. Chronic mental depression and the need to earn more money, prompting many to work extremely long hours, set the stage for an epidemic of stimulant dependency. By 1954, perhaps 5 percent of the Japanese urban population between the ages of fifteen and twenty-five were dependent upon Methedrine. In an effort to combat this drain on its manpower, Japan imposed strict controls on the availability of stimulants.

A milk truck's innocent exterior concealed this illicit drug factory, one of more than 150 such clandestine laboratories seized by U.S. investigators since 1966. Others were found in suburban basements, tenement attics and remote mountain cabins.

The first medical use of methamphetamine also stemmed from German research that preceded the war. In addition to studying its ability to combat fatigue, German clinicians investigated the drug's capacity to counteract depression in patients recovering from operations. This aspect of the drug's action attracted the attention of an English pharmaceutical company, and, in 1943, it marketed a methamphetamine crystal called Methedrine. This crystal, which is dissolved and injected rather than swallowed, helped prevent and treat shock caused by surgery. The drug's stimulant properties also helped to maintain blood pressure at a safe level during operations.

In 1969, however, the original American manufacturer of Methedrine withdrew it from the market because of the mounting misuse of the drug by people seeking the exhilaration of a high. Benzedrine nasal inhalers have also been discontinued because of harmful side effects. Many people developed a dependency upon the mental uplift the drug seemed to bring.

Today legitimate amphetamine production in the United States consists mainly of tablets and capsules. About eight billion of these stimulants are produced annually, enough to provide each American with at least 40 pills. It is estimated that perhaps 50 percent of these legally manufactured capsules are diverted into other than medical channels.

Moreover, the medical value of amphetamines is seriously being questioned. At present doctors prescribe amphetamine derivatives to alleviate mild depressions due to grief, senility or recovery from illness, to combat excessive drowsiness caused by sedatives and to curb appetite in persons who are overweight. These drugs are also used to treat two rare ailments: Parkinson's disease and narcolepsy (the tendency to fall asleep at any time).

In certain special cases, physicians will prescribe amphetamines to combat fatigue. Astronauts, pilots, soldiers and others involved in dangerous tasks that require prolonged alertness and concentration are sometimes issued these stimulants.

However, doubts that amphetamines constitute the best treatment for these conditions are increasing. Dr. John D. Griffith, instructor of pharmacology at the Vanderbilt School of Medicine, testified before Congress that the "problem now being considered . . . is whether the benefits derived from amphetamines outweigh their toxicity. It is the consensus of the world scientific literature that the amphetamines are of very little benefit to mankind."

According to research conducted by Dr. Griffith, the value of amphetamines as a weight control is extremely short-lived. He observed that "studies show subjects will lose an average of 6.75 pounds during a course of treatment . . . using amphetamines. [This is the] total weight loss during an entire six-to-twenty-week period. At the end of six weeks, usually, the patient becomes resistant to the effects of amphetamines and derives little or no further benefit."

Dr. Griffith also rejected the use of amphetamines to combat mild depressions. He told the House Select Committee on Crime that the "antidepressant effect of amphetamines is very brief— on the order of days." Then a tolerance develops and continued use of the drug brings on the risk of dependence and severe depression.

Other scientific authorities report findings which substantiate those of Dr. Griffith. In 1968, the National Research Council of the National Academy of Sciences recommended that amphetamines only be included in the treatment of two diseases— narcolepsy and hyperkinetic behavior in children. The Council also suggested that limited use in the early stages of weight control might be beneficial. According to the Council report, reducing the medical need for amphetamines would limit production and thus restrict the amount available for overuse. Curbing legitimate prescription of these drugs also would reduce the possibility of accidental dependency.

Many housewives, teen-agers and college students develop such a dependency on diet pills that contain amphetamines. They continue to take the pills long after their usefulness as a weight control has worn off and then go to another diet doctor for more. These persons usually depend on the drug for the mental and physical lift it seems to bring.

Overly tired people often take amphetamines to ward off fatigue. In fact the ability of amphetamines to mask weariness and prolong exertion has prompted their extensive use as "pep pills" by truck drivers, students, athletes and businessmen.

UP AND DOWN DRUGS

Classes of Legitimate Drugs Brand names	Description or Slang names	Medical Usage
SEDATIVES	Sleeping pills, goof balls	Sedatives are used to induce sleep and relaxation. They are used to treat insomnia, anxiety, tension, high blood pressure, convulsions, epileptic seizures and mental disorders.
Barbiturates Seconal (sodium secobarbital)	Red Birds, Red Devils	
Nembutal (sodium pentobarbital)	Yellow Jackets	
Luminal (phenobarbital)	Purple Hearts	
Amytal (sodium amobarbital)	Blue Heavens, Blue Devils	
Nonbarbiturates Doriden (glutethimide)	Goofers	(same as above)
Noludar		
Chloral Hydrate	Knock-out drops Mickey Finn (when mixed with alcohol)	
STIMULANTS	Pep pills	Amphetamines depress appetite and are used in weight control as diet pills. They are used to combat fatigue and prod alertness; to alleviate depression by elevating moods; to treat narcoleps: hyperkineticism, and other neurological diseas:
Amphetamines Benzedrine (amphetamine sulfate)	Bennies, Ups	
Dexedrine (dextroamphetamine sulfate)	Dexies, Dex	
Methedrine (methamphetamine)	Speed, Crystal, Meth	
Dexamyl	combination of amphetamines and a sedative	Dexamyl is used to treat mild depression.
PAIN-RELIEVERS *Opium Derivatives* Morphine	Dope, M opium derivative	relieves severe pain
Codeine	Schoolboy, Dope opium derivative	relieves minor pain and coughing
Paregoric	P.G., P.O. contains opium	counteracts diarrhea used as a sedative
Dilaudid	opium derivative	relieves pain

Effects Physical Psychological	Dangers
Sedatives depress the central nervous system. Other effects include muscle relaxation, impaired coordination, slowed reaction time, drowsiness, staggering, alterations of space perceptions. Loss of judgment & self-control, quick temper, incoherence, depression and slurred speech may occur.	All barbiturates are addictive. Severe illness occurs if these drugs are withdrawn. Overdosage or rapid injection can cause blood pressure to drop, respiratory failure—coma or death. Combined with excessive alcohol they can cause coma or death. Seconal—caution advised if liver is impaired. Nembutal should not be used if liver is damaged since it is eliminated through the liver. If Nembutal is withdrawn abruptly, convulsions may occur.
(same as above)	Doriden poisoning is difficult to treat. Highly addictive.
Amphetamines stimulate central nervous system. They produce insomnia, restlessness, euphoria, irritability, excitability, and tremors. Chronic use results in extreme weight loss, delusions, hallucinations, overconfidence.	After heavy prolonged use of amphetamines there is: tendency to be violent under delusions; susceptibility to severe exhaustion, malnutrition, pneumonia; possible development of high blood pressure, heart malfunction, brain damage; dependency; severe depressions if amphetamines are withdrawn. Methedrine, when injected in high doses, may cause hallucinations, heart attacks. Danger of infections from needles.
Opium derivatives depress the central nervous system; are known as narcotics. They impair intellectual function and coordination; can cause drowsiness, euphoria, nausea, itching, loss of appetite.	highly addictive narcotic, severe withdrawal pain; overdose can cause death.
	addictive
	addictive: same dangers as morphine

Classes of Legitimate Drugs Brand names	Description or Slang names	Medical Usage
PAIN-RELIEVERS **Non-Opiates** Methadone	synthetic morphine-type drug	kills strong pain
Demerol	synthetic opiate	relieves pain sometimes used in childbirth
Meperidine	synthetic morphine-type drug	relieves pain
Percodan		relieves strong pain
Darvon	synthetic pain-killer	relieves minor pain, usually chronic or recurrent pains
TRANQUILIZERS **Phenothiazine Compounds** Thorazine Compazine Stelazine	major tranquilizers chlorpromazine	used to treat severe psychiatric conditions; relieve major anxiety; used as sedatives before surgery Thorazine suppresses hallucinations caused by LSD.
Reserpine Compounds Rauwolfia	major tranquilizers	(same as above)
Equanil, Miltown (meprobamate) Librium (chlordiazepoxide)	minor tranquilizers	used to treat mild anxiety, tensions, minor emotional disorders; used to slow down over-active individuals; used to relax muscles
Valium (diazepam)		(same as above)
ANTI-DEPRESSANTS **Dibenzapines** Tofranil Elavil		used to relieve moderate to severe depressions
Monoamine Oxidase Drugs Marplan Nardil Parnate Eutonyl Niamid	MAO inhibitors each has different chemical formula	used to alleviate depression—usually if no other drug is effective

Effects Physical Psychological	Dangers
	addictive
	addictive: more difficult to treat Demerol addiction than morphine
High doses cause excitement, tremors, convulsions.	
	addictive
	non-addictive: some people develop dependencies, however
Drowsiness, blurry vision, skin rash and tremors may occur. Mental sluggishness, . disturbed sleep and depression may result after prolonged use.	Use of tranquilizers should not be discontinued abruptly. Non-addictive, but thorazine may be dangerous for liver and bone marrow. The combined effect of thorazine and the hallucinogen STP can be fatal—should not be used to tone down STP panic reactions.
	may be addictive
Valium does not usually cause drowsiness or loss of alertness.	may cause physical dependence resulting in severe withdrawal symptoms
elevation of moods stimulation	
	Constant medical supervision required with MAO drugs; may have toxic effects on liver, brain, heart and blood vessels; should not be combined with strong pain relievers or taken after eating certain foods such as cheese.

This type of pill-popping is usually infrequent, but even occasional use can be hazardous.

Many long-distance truckers purchase stimulants to remain awake during an entire trip. The "Los Angeles Turnaround," which is a long-acting capsule of amphetamine sulphate, is one such pill. Supposedly, swallowing these pills at regular intervals enables a driver to complete a trip from Los Angeles to New York and back without sleeping. According to Dr. Sidney Cohen, Director of the Division of Narcotic Addiction and Drug Abuse, National Institute of Mental Health, many truck accidents result directly from the use of stimulants. Many drivers fall asleep for a few seconds as the result of taking high doses. Others experience hallucinations which can cause them to veer off the road or to crash into another vehicle.

Students cramming for exams and businessmen working long hours often resort to stimulants to sustain a level of activity beyond their usual endurance. Athletes occasionally use amphetamines to provoke sudden spurts of energy. However, these spurts are sometimes accompanied by collapse or sudden death. In an attempt to prevent such accidents, sporting associations have banned the use of these drugs.

Another and more dangerous use of these stimulants has become popular among drug experimenters. An increasing number of young people are swallowing, sniffing and injecting large amounts of amphetamines, usually methamphetamine or "speed," in their search for exhilaration and euphoria. Particularly heavy use occurs among former heavy LSD users or "acid heads." According to Dr. David E. Smith of the Haight-Ashbury Free Clinic, the explanation "I took too much acid (LSD)so I took heroin or speed to get my head straight" is a common one. Amphetamines are also apparently used by "acid heads" to prolong, intensify or reactivate an LSD experience.

Since it is the most widely abused of these drugs, its nature and effects may in many respects serve as a model for the others. On their path to "speed" many of these experimenters begin by swallowing amphetamine tablets. They may start with small doses of ten to twenty milligrams and build up. Heavy users or "speed freaks" often inject from 500 to 1,000 milligrams at one time.

According to research conducted by Dr. James Carey, a sociologist at the University of California, taking more than the usually prescribed ten milligrams can produce pronounced changes in consciousness and behavior. Heightened awareness and energy change to extreme nervousness and apprehension. The individual begins to fidget, finding it impossible to remain still. Reactions to close-range events are enhanced but the user becomes so engrossed in the immediate that he loses awareness of everything else.

Dr. Carey recorded the impressions of one "speed" user who remarked that "all the time (we were listening to the radio, talking and drawing) I had no idea what was going on in the other side of the room, whether people were arguing or . . . crying."

This research also revealed that chronic users of methamphetamine usually prefer to inject it because of the sudden "flash" or "rush" that envelops the body seconds after the drug has entered the bloodstream. Some compare it to an electric shock. One girl said her whole brain seemed to be vibrating and that shocks like adrenalin surged up and down her spine.

Most heavy users consider the rush an intensely pleasurable experience. It is also dangerous and sometimes fatal. Physically injection produces a sudden rise in blood pressure, which may cause cerebral hemorrhages or heart failure. Discovery of this danger has led many users to wear "Danger—Speed Kills" buttons in an attempt to warn others away from the drug. Occasionally overdoses produce a feeling of numbness instead of a "rush." Many tell of feeling paralyzed after injecting "speed"—afraid to move as their hearts throbbed and their thoughts stopped. Others felt as though their minds were racing out of control.

The practice of injecting shot after shot of methamphetamine in order to enjoy the rush and remain "high" is known as a "speed run." Some amphetamine addicts stay awake as long as a week. They may lose as much as ten or twenty pounds since both appetite and the desire to sleep are almost completely suppressed.

On the psychic level, massive doses of methamphetamine

breed obsessive compulsions and distort concentration. Most users become intrinsically involved in a single complex task since the ability to focus attention, although greatly enhanced, is on a narrow plane. Drawing may occupy the individual for hours, yet the finished product is usually a meaningless jumble of tiny objects and intricate lines that conveys little to the observer beyond a feeling of enormous energy and wasted time.

Attempts to perform normal tasks are frequently warped by the drug's effects on perception. One youth tried to repair a radio while under the influence of amphetamines. In the process, he dismantled twelve others, none of which was broken, and could not put any of them back together. Students who take "speed" in order to enhance their ability to study have been known to memorize whole textbooks. Some, however, suddenly "click off" during the exam, and are unable to remember a single fact. One college student wrote an entire essay on the same line of the test booklet.

Although he is able to concentrate for long periods of time, the user is also easily distracted. This leads to rapid mood changes and relative indifference to those around him. Methamphetamine sends a person speeding through most situations so quickly that he reacts almost without thinking. His dealings with others, therefore, remain on a very superficial level.

Prolonged use of methamphetamine wears the body out and often provokes violent outbursts. The results of research conducted at the University of California indicate that abrupt changes of mood, often accompanied by violent actions, occur more frequently as the body deteriorates physically. Irritability induced by exhaustion may cause the "speed" addict to lash out in response to imagined insults or minor inconveniences, especially if he has gone without food and sleep for a week.

Persons who inject huge amounts of "speed" over long periods of time also frequently develop delusions of persecution and other symptoms of paranoia. An amphetamine addict often suspects that everyone he sees knows exactly what he is thinking. He will report fears that rooms will collapse around him if he enters, or that everyone he meets—and everyone he has not met—is plotting to kill him.

Heavy "speeding" also produces hallucinations. One user,

quoted in Carey's study of methamphetamine abuse, remarked, "I quit because I was seeing movies of myself projected on all the walls in my apartment, only I was the only person in the room and there was no camera." Others look at themselves and see vermin swarming all over their skin. Some believe their bodies are pockmarked with huge scars and holes.

Research conducted by Dr. P. H. Connell among forty-two British patients reported strong similarities between the mental illness, schizophrenia, and the psychoses produced by amphetamines. In both, the victim suffers from delusions of persecution and strong hallucinations in settings that seem normal to others.

There is also evidence that the chronic use of large amounts of these stimulants may cause brain cell damage. During the epidemic of amphetamine abuse that swept Japan in the fifties, many heavily dependent individuals suffered from severe memory gaps, chronic confusion and an inability to discern time or place.

One researcher, Dr. Everett Ellinwood, of Duke University School of Medicine, remarked that "chronic states of exhaustion such as those caused by extensive use of amphetamines can cause brain cell damage."

Evidence indicates that many of the young amphetamine users or "speed freaks" that inhabit San Francisco's Haight-Ashbury and other drug subcultures seem unable to think clearly or remember recent events after months of regular dependency upon methamphetamine.

No matter how long a speed run lasts, it is followed inevitably by the crash, which may actually obliterate memory of the days which preceded it. Deep sleep due to total exhaustion may last as long as 48 hours. Upon awakening, the individual feels depressed and hungry. Head-aching misery turns small demands upon his attention into severe annoyances. Arguments, occasionally culminating in blows, occur for seemingly insignificant reasons.

A "speed freak" will often prolong runs even when totally exhausted in order to avoid the "rebound" depression that occurs as the drug's effects diminish. However, amphetamine addicts increasingly are using sleeping pills to bring them down slowly and put them to sleep. When they awake, many return to speed in order to eliminate sedative "hangovers" and depression. This practice often leads to a dangerous cycle of drug dependence upon both "up" and "down" drugs.

Although the user does build up a tolerance to amphetamines and so must take larger and larger amounts to maintain his high, it was long believed that speed did not cause physical addiction. Recent studies of users during the "crash" stage of a speed trip indicate otherwise. The painful physical symptoms suffered by crashers are apparently a form of withdrawal. Reinjecting amphetamines will cause these symptoms to subside immediately. Consequently, many scientists and doctors now believe that physical addiction to regular heavy use of amphetamines does occur.

Other physical complications can result from heavy sustained "speeding" on amphetamines. Speed gnaws at the body, consuming energy which is not replaced because the individual refuses to eat while he is high. The result is usually severe malnutrition.

Sometimes a sober glimpse of his emaciated image in the mirror is enough to make a chronic speeder stop. If not, the nervous tremors and twitches, the teeth grinding, the severe muscle and joint pains which inevitably result may convince the user to quit. Tooth abcesses, ulcers and skin infections also develop as a person's resistance wears down.

Injecting methamphetamine invites infectious disease. According to federal statistics, a chronic user has better than a 50-percent chance of contracting hepatitis. The infection may arise from the direct impact of hugh amounts of amphetamines upon the liver or from contaminated needles.

The extent of unprescribed amphetamine use in the United States is difficult to determine. One survey revealed that 21 percent of all students had tried these stimulants. However, most were infrequent users who had actually obtained their pep pills from the family medicine cabinet. The number of older adults dependent upon pill-popping is not known, but indiscriminate use is believed to be widespread.

The practice of "speed shooting" among younger drug experimenters appears to be on the rise. This aspect of amphetamine abuse has prompted intensive research into its long-range effects on body and mind.

The government is sponsoring several projects to determine whether chronic body or brain damage results from heavy sustained use of amphetamine stimulants. These federally-supported studies include projects to explore the effects of amphetamines upon brain functions and behavior, to determine the physical consequences of chronic long-term use and to investigate postamphetamine depression.

Congressional hearings on amphetamines, conducted in 1969, already have concluded that the chronic abuse of these drugs "involves more people than . . . heroin and that their effects upon the personality can be as dangerous," if not more so.

The sedatives calm instead of excite. Commonly called "downs," these drugs depress the central nervous system and dull the user's sense perceptions. The more potent sedatives relax tension and eventually induce sleep, while the milder tranquilizers quiet anxiety without causing excessive drowsiness. Many high-strung individuals depend upon these drugs to take the edge off grating tensions and, at times, provide temporary oblivion.

Dr. Stanley F. Yolles, former director of the National Institute of Mental Health, testifying before Congress, placed the number of persons using prescribed sedatives at close to 20 million. He also estimated that perhaps 20 percent of all college students have tried these drugs.

According to many experts, sedatives and tranquilizers have become the temporary solution to all problems resulting from mental and emotional tension. Persons seeking relief from nervous disorders invariably receive sedatives as the initial treatment. Unfortunately prolonged regular use of these drugs can lead to severe dependency and, occasionally, to fatal overdoses. In fact, the number of deaths due to barbiturate or tranquilizer overdosage exceeds 3,000 each year. Moreover, Dr. Sidney Cohen has reported that "barbiturates are the most commonly employed chemical mode of committing suicide in the United States today."

The barbiturates, which are salts derived from barbituric acid, are some of the most potent as well as the most popular tension-relievers available. First synthesized in 1912, these drugs soon superseded all others as the most commonly prescribed sedatives.

The barbiturate family encompasses a wide range of pills which vary greatly in impact and method of action. Nembutal (yellow jackets) and Seconal (red birds) are quick acting, short-lived depressants. The "purple hearts"—phenobarbital (Luminal)—amobarbital (Amytal) and butabarbital (Butisol) start slowly but have a longer, stronger effect. The effect of these capsules can range from mild relaxation and sleep to deep coma and death, according to the amount administered. Most other sedatives act in similar ways to relax body functioning and are evaluated according to their similarities to or differences from the barbiturate group.

Barbiturates act to relax physical functioning on several levels. They slow the action of nerves, skeletal muscles, and heart muscles, relax nervous stomachs and slow the rate of respiration. These depressants can be used to control convulsions and are frequently included in the treatment of epilepsy.

In moderate, prescribed amounts, sedatives merely relax the user and usually put him to sleep. Higher doses, however, cause deep depression, slurred speech, staggering, and other loss of coordination. Memory and thinking are impaired. Confusion and sometimes amnesia result. Many heavy users forget how many pills they have taken. They may sleep several hours, awaken in a stupor and take some more. Accidental death resulting from unintentional overdosage is common among barbiturate addicts.

The chronic user may be quarrelsome, irritable and short-tempered. To the casual onlooker, he often appears drunk. Many barbiturate addicts hurt themselves or others after losing physical or emotional control.

Heavy tolerance to the barbiturates can develop. According to Dr. Cohen, habits of more than 50 sleeping pills (5000 mg.) a day have been recorded. Chronic users often experience a switch in the drug's effects as a result of prolonged use. Instead of slowing down or sleeping, the addict feels "high," "away," or "calm." He feels more alive and better able to cope with his problems. These feelings are usually signs of strong physical addiction to the sedative.

Withdrawing an addict from barbiturate dependence is a highly dangerous and difficult task. Severe cramps, nausea, convulsions and delirium occur when the addict is denied his drug. Dizzy spells, insomnia and extreme anxiety are frequent symptoms. Sudden withdrawal can be fatal. Thus, the process of destroying dependency must be accomplished slowly and under the close care of a physician. Even when proper steps are taken to ensure relatively safe withdrawal, months of recovery are necessary before the user can function normally.

Tranquilizers, although milder in effect than the barbiturates, can also produce pronounced psychological and, in some cases, physical dependency. Meprobamate (Equanil, Miltown), chlordiazepinol (Librium) and diazepan (Valium), which are fairly recent medical discoveries, are increasingly replacing sedatives in the treatment of minor nervous disorders. They also are frequently used to quiet agitated patients in mental hospitals. Theoretically these tranquilizers should reduce anxiety and tension without affecting mental alertness and physical coordination. Unfortunately the perfect tranquilizer does not exist. Mental and physical functioning is somewhat impaired even when moderate doses of these mild tension relievers are administered.

"Pill-heads" on tranquilizers often appear drowsy, apathetic and listless. Tremors, lack of coordination and, sometimes, seizures occur as dependence develops. In most respects, dependence on tranquilizers is similar to but much milder than barbiturate addiction.

As is the case with legally available pep pills, the extent of barbiturate and tranquilizer misuse is difficult to calculate. This is due greatly to the lack of control over the production of these drugs and the huge quantities that are manufactured each year.

According to statistics compiled by the U.S. Department of Commerce, American pharmaceutical companies manufacture enough sedatives to provide each person with six to eight capsules yearly. For amphetamines, their figures indicate an annual production level of four to five pills per person. Other calculations indicate that the total amount of sedatives and tranquilizers produced each year exceeds 10 billion. Combined with the annual amphetamine production of 8 billion pills, this means a total exceeding 100 pills per person. Over half of these find their way into the hands of people—both in the United States and abroad—who have developed some kind of dependency.

The full extent of pill dependency in the United States is still unknown, but current trends are causing increasing alarm among government officials and medical experts. Housewives, businessmen, students, athletes and others have become unwittingly vulnerable to pill dependency. Furthermore, many younger adolescents, searching for some sort of drug high, are popping pills from family medicine cabinets.

According to Dr. Yolles, the excessive use of stimulant and sedative drugs outranks dependency on any other class of mood-altering chemical. Or, as one high-ranking government official remarked, Americans seem to be on a "collective trip," of which "the individual and social costs have yet to be calculated." This supports the view that Americans are living in the midst of a drug culture.

CHAPTER THREE

The Hallucinogens

The term "hallucinogen" refers to any drug "capable of producing perceptual alterations up to hallucinations, intense emotional changes of wide variations, a nonrational, reverie type of thinking and ego distortions such as loss of self and feelings of complete strangeness." Marihuana, LSD and mescaline all belong to this category, as do the products of more than forty naturally occurring plant species in the Americas. Some, like marihuana, have a history stretching back over 4,000 years. Others, like LSD, were first available in the 1960s, and similar chemical syntheses are still coming from the laboratory. But old or new, they are described as the "mind drugs," and less is known or understood about their effects than those of any other group.

The most famous of these is marihuana. According to the United Nations, its rate of international consumption is second only to that of alcohol, but until five years ago, it was never widely used in the United States. Today, the House Select Committee on Crime reports that there are 3 million *regular* users in this country, and official estimates of the number who have experimented with the drug at least once range up to 20 million.

Even more striking has been the change in the average user. In 1944, most came from the lowest socio-economic classes, and the majority were Negroes and Latin Americans. Today, use of the drug has become so general that students in one affluent Long Island suburb were astonished to find that only 46 percent of their high school population had sampled marihuana. Other surveys conducted for the National Institute of Mental Health report the growing prevalence of drugs in West Coast colleges and high schools. In 1967, 18 percent of students questioned had tried marihuana. By 1968, their proportion had increased to 57 percent. And it was predicted that 70 percent of these students would have tried marihuana by spring, 1969, despite heavy legal penalties.

If marihuana (or "pot," "grass," "tea," "weed," "maryjane" and "reefer") did not always enjoy such widespread popularity in this country, neither did it enjoy such a sensational reputation. George Washington grew it as a valuable hemp crop, and for many years, pharmacies kept a bottle of the plant's extract to give corn remedies an attractive green color. It was not until jazz musicians began using the drug after World War I that marihuana became associated with the sordid implications of "smoking dope" in big city slums. Now, in view of its growing popularity among the young, it seems essential to attempt to disentangle the drug once more from its legend.

Marihuana and its more powerful version, hashish, come from the resin of the unfertilized female hemp plant and, to a lesser degree, from the male. Resin is the plant's protection against the harmful effects of too much sun, so it is found in greatest concentration in the flowering tops. The resin of the leaves and flowering shoots is both sparser and of a poorer quality. The seeds contain no resin and, after being specially deactivated for growth, are sold commercially as birdseed. The drug products of the hemp are sometimes known as cannabis from the plant's Latin name, *cannabis sativa*. Indigenous to Central Asia, marihuana now grows wild in virtually every country in the temperate and tropical zones of the world. But conditions of high temperatures, large amounts of sunlight and low humidity produce the purest grade of resin.

Marihuana and hashish may be smoked or eaten. Most commonly, the dried chopped leaves, stems and flowering tops of the plant are rolled into a cigarette-form known as a "joint," "weed," "reefer" or "stick." The result is distinguishable from regular tobacco because cannabis retains its bright green color and its smoke has an acrid sweet scent. Incense is often used in conjunction with marihuana to veil this distinctive aroma. Other essential paraphernalia for the smoker include a variety of papers for rolling the joint, "roach clips," water pipes, and special miniature "toking" pipes. The favorite paper for smokers is plain white Zig-Zag, but licorice, chocolate and strawberry flavored papers are also popular because they give the smoke a candied taste, and lessen its harshness. The "roach" is the butt of the cigarette, and delicately designed clips enable the smoker to finish the end of the hot, fast-burning substance. Water pipes pass the smoke over cooling water and are considered to be less wasteful since most of the smoke is trapped between inhalations. They may be elaborate, oriental "hookahs" or simple combinations of a coffee can and aluminum foil. The "toking" pipe is identified by its tiny bowl. (A "toke" is an inhalation.) If the pipe is to be used for hashish, a minute piece of window screening is placed over the bowl, and the cannabis resin in its dry powdered form is placed on top, then lit. For those who dislike smoking, the "underground" press publishes recipes for chili pot, pot meat ball, spaghetti sauce, cookies and brownies based on the drug.

In its most powerful form, cannabis is outlawed by every country in the civilized world, and its sale is punishable by death in Nigeria and Egypt. But the comparative weakness of the U.S. grade of marihuana has led to the argument that it is "harmless." Investigators respond that they simply do not yet know. The active element in both marihuana and hashish—tetrahydrocannabinol, or THC, was first isolated in 1942, but was not successfully synthesized until 1965. This meant that for the first time a standardized dosage was available for experimental studies. Although a full scientific report on cannabis from the National Institute of Mental Health will not be ready for another two to three years, some findings have long been common knowledge.

Scientific studies have determined that marihuana must contain 2 percent or more THC content to be potent. The THC content of U.S. marihuana varies from about .05 percent to 1.5

percent. The Mexican variety's content ranges from 2 to 4 percent. The Middle Eastern and South East Asian products are often more potent due to a greater abundance of hemp or to careful methods of cultivation. By contrast, the THC content in any variety of hashish may range as high as 20 percent.

The psychological effects of marihuana upon the user vary greatly. What the "pot" or "hash" smoker experiences depends on several factors: his personality; his expectations concerning the drug; his surroundings at the time of use; the potency of the dose; and the way the dose is consumed. Effects of the drug vary not only among different individuals, but the same individual can experience profoundly different highs according to his mood, his anxieties and his fears at the time.

When marihuana is smoked, the effects normally begin within a half hour and last from two to three hours. However, when marihuana is eaten in some form, the drug's effects may be delayed as much as two or three hours and can last perhaps six hours.

For the novice, a marihuana "high" may begin with either no sensations, or extreme emotional reactions like uncontrollable laughter or tears. However, most experienced users report feelings of great contentment and relaxation, of "flowing past reality," of increased self-awareness and a greater sense of fellowship with companions. If the dose is powerful enough, it can lead to visual hallucinations, an increased sensitivity to sound and the experience of synesthesia ("tasting" colors, "seeing" music). Some users experience a wavelike sense of reality—every person and object in the room seems to be sending out "vibrations" which the smoker can receive and interpret. Frequently, the user will be convinced that he is thinking more clearly and enjoying a far deeper insight into the nature of things while "stoned" on the drug. Other common reactions include very uncomfortable experiences of terrifying anxiety or paranoia that are beyond the reach of rational control. Even during bad experiences, however, time and space are distorted by being stretched out, so that even experienced users do not advise doing anything that involves "real" perception like driving a car.

Marihuana and hashish also produce certain immediate physical effects in the user. The severity of these symptoms depends upon the potency and quantity of the drug and upon the individual. The pupils become dilated and the whites of the eyes, bloodshot. Other common effects reported are: a very rapid pulse rate; raised blood pressure; more rapid breathing; chills; drowsiness; burning feelings in the throat and lungs; nausea; diarrhea; hunger or thirst. Physically, the drug has been reported as both a stimulant and a depressant and has proved peculiarly elusive to medical researchers. According to Dr. Milton Joffe, chief of the Drug Sciences Division at the Bureau of Narcotics and Dangerous Drugs:

"As soon as a compound is ingested in almost any form, whether it is ingested orally or smoked, even though it has a known THC content, THC itself does not appear in the blood. It has passed through the circulation and it becomes something else. The problem has been to identify what this something else is."

Researchers now think they know what THC may become, but as yet the long-range physical effects of the drug are unknown, because they are unmeasurable.

However, there have been reports of acute psychosis occurring when a large quantity of potent cannabis has been consumed. These reports are complicated by the fact that, in earlier times, the drug has been especially attractive to those classified as emotionally immature or unstable. Hence, the Indian Hemp-Drug Commission in 1894 concluded that "excessive use of the hemp drugs indicates and intensifies mental instability" although they felt that moderate use was safer on the whole than alcohol. Another report on drug use in Morocco showed that over a two-year period 25 percent of the male admissions to one psychiatric hospital had been admitted as cannabis psychoses. It found that most of the symptoms in these patients tended to disappear gradually after a few months, except for those in one category: cannabis deterioration. This was found in chronic, long-time users and was characterized by "precocious senility and overall physical and mental deterioration." According to the researcher, Dr. Ahmed Benabud, "These are the old addicts, exuberant, friendly, kif-happy vagabonds, often oddly dressed and living by begging." Others argue that the prevalence of severe mental illness is no greater among cannabis users than among the general population, but according to Dr. William H. McGlothlin, a former Rand Corporation psychologist who reviewed the Moroccan situation and others like it:

> It is clear from Eastern descriptions that gross personality changes do result from very prolonged and excessive use of cannabis. The complete loss of ambition and the neglect of personal habits, dress, and hygiene resemble characteristics of the skid-row alcoholic in this country.

While the cannabis drugs are not physically addicting, they do seem to produce a "psychic dependence" in some users. According to Dr. Helen H. Nowlis, author of *Drugs on the College Campus,* "Serious drug involvement is . . . seldom consistent with serious work." Other U.S. doctors, noting the confused speech and irrational thinking associated with marihuana use, are attempting to identify and establish the existence of these symptoms in an effort to find out whether heavy users tend to "drop out" because they want to or because they must. Recent findings reported by the National Institute of Mental Health (NIMH) have verified in some marihuana users:

- alteration in sequential thought (Reese Jones)
- speech impairment due to the loss of immediate recall and the difficulty in the retrieval of recently acquired information (A. T. Weil and U. E. Zinberg)
- impairment on psychological testing which was interpreted as due to decreased mental abilities (Hollister et al.)
- significant impairment of short-term memory (the recall of events that had occurred during the preceding few seconds was disrupted) (Melges et al.)
- occurrence of "flashback" effects after the initial effects of marihuana use had disappeared (M. H. Keeler)
- instances of toxic psychotic reactions lasting 1 to 11 days from smoking Vietnamese material (J. A. Talbott et al.)
- anxiety, paranoid states, depression, rage reactions, inability to concentrate or psychotic breaks (L. Wurmser et al.)
- "Decreased drive, apathy, distractability, poor judgment,

introversion, depersonalization, diminished capacity to carry out complex plans or prepare realistically for the future, magical thinking, a peculiar fragmentation of thought and progressive loss of insight" (L. J. West)

These findings indicate with certainty that for a few people, at least, marihuana is not a "harmless weed." But according to Dr. Stanley Yolles, recent director of NIMH, their real significance lies in whether "repeated episodes of bizarre thinking, dreamlike states, self-removal from life situations, interference with recent recall, all in the context of euphoria, result in a sustained disinclination to become involved in logical, rational thinking." He hazarded the guess that "the constant user may indeed come to prefer nonrational thinking to problem solving."

It may take another five to ten years of extensive research before scientists reach a consensus about the measurable effects of cannabis on the human system. Like tobacco and alcohol, however, many feel that the hemp plant drugs may well produce some lasting damage.

Today, cannabis is widely recognized as the mildest of the hallucinogenic drugs, although it is capable of producing virtually all of the effects of other, far stronger drugs in this group. The rest of the hallucinogens are generally known as the "exotic" drugs because they are far less prevalent.

Psychedelic (mind-changing) or psychoactive drugs were commonly used in many ancient civilizations, where their existence in nature was celebrated as the "flesh of the gods." Some 3,000 years ago, according to Eastern legend, a consciousness-expanding substance called "soma" was involved in the origins of yoga. In Mexico, there is evidence that the Aztecs incorporated "transcendental" drug plants into their religious ceremonies in order to commune with the gods or to provoke visions as early as 300 B.C. Another drug group, the Solanaceae, rose to prominence in the sixteenth century when European witches used Thorn Apple, belladonna, mandragora or henbane plant preparations to induce vivid visions.

The use of these psychoactive substances, including morning glory seeds, psilocybin from a Mexican mushroom, and mescaline from the peyote cactus, have been regulated by law in the United States since 1966. But an exception was made for the some 200,000 members of the Native American Church, who are Peyote cultists. The membership of this Christianized sect is drawn from nearly every Indian tribe across the nation, and they follow an elaborate purification ritual including steam baths, the abstinence from salt and the adoption of attitudes of total sincerity, humility and truthfulness before each ceremonial rite. Their cactus buttons are consumed under the guidance of a leader, and the members claim to experience direct revelations from God. As one of the early leaders described it: "The white man goes into his church house and talks *about* Jesus; the Indian goes into his tepee and talks to Jesus."

The undoubted sincerity of such claims has puzzled numerous anthropologists, psychologists and federal officials, but after many years of debate, the Indians' right to the drug was ruled constitutional in 1960. In his decision, the presiding judge wrote that:

> There is nothing debasing or morally reprehensible about the Peyote ritual. . . . The use of Peyote is essential to the existence of the Peyote religion. Without it, the practice of religion would be effectively prevented. The manner in which Peyote is used by the Indian worshipper is not inconsistent with the public health, morals or welfare. Its use, in the manner disclosed by the evidence in this case, is in fact entirely consistent with the good morals, health and spiritual elevation of some 225,000 Indians.

The peyote cactus grows wild in the southwest of the United States and in Mexico. The plant is small, topped by a spineless gray-green "button" that is covered with fuzzy white hairs. The psychedelic alkaloids of peyote are concentrated in the button. It may be eaten raw or brewed in a tea. Sometimes the buttons are dried and powdered to be placed in gelatin capsules. Since the methods of preparing peyote are crude, the strength of the active alkaloids vary from one plant to the next. Thus it is difficult to measure exact doses and their corresponding effect on different individuals.

Mescaline is the principal psychoactive substance (alkaloid) in peyote. It produces the vivid and colorful imagery often experienced and emphasized by peyote eaters. There are other alkaloids in peyote, however, which interact to produce different effects from those provoked by mescaline alone.

Raw peyote powder usually causes nausea, trembling and perspiration. These physical symptoms occur one or two hours after peyote is eaten and normally subside as the psychological phenomena begin. Swallowing or injecting synthetic mescaline will cause similar, often more intense, mental effects with less physical discomfort.

The mind-alterations attributed to peyote and mescaline are similar to those caused by LSD, only milder. A dreamlike intoxicated state usually occurs, typically characterized by vivid and colorful images. Most often these are geometric images or other kaleidoscopic combinations of shapes. Pure mescaline, particularly, produces vivid imagery. Among some Indians the drug is used as an inspiration for bead-work patterns. Following a period of heightened awareness and other phenomena, the user falls into a deep sleep.

Although more than 1,000 documents have been written on the use and effects of mescaline since it was synthesized in 1896, little more is understood of the drug than of the other hallucinogens. The National Institute of Mental Health reports that currently no research projects on the drug are being funded despite its growing popularity among the young. Since its visionary effects are supposed to be gentler and less "out of control" than those of the more powerful psychedelics, it is becoming increasingly sought after by students, sometimes with tragic results.

One 20-year-old Florida youth, before committing suicide, summed up his experience with what he thought was mescaline, writing, "My mind is no longer my friend. It won't leave me alone." He related in a note he left behind: "This Christmas I had a very bad experience with drug called mescaline. I have smoked a little pot before—as [have] many my age—but I tried mescaline only once. . . . Since then I have not been in control of my mind. I have killed myself because I can no longer run my own affairs, and I can only be trouble and worry to those who love and care for me.

"I have tried to straighten myself out, but things are only getting worse.

"There is nothing but misery for all of us should I allow myself to deteriorate further.

"To those of my friends who might also think about learning about themselves with mind-expanding drugs—don't.

"Learn about yourself as you live your life—don't try to know everything at once by swallowing a pill. It could be too much for your mind to handle at one time. It could blow out all the circuits as it did with me. . . ."

When questioned, officials in Washington said they doubted that the drug which provoked these effects could have been mescaline, but the incident spotlights one of the greatest risks with all of the "exotic" drugs: they are illegal and must be purchased from black-market sources. For this reason, their origins are always totally obscure to the purchaser, who must buy on faith. One recent survey of more than twenty-five samples of "mescaline" collected from street dealers revealed varying mixtures of lactose, LSD, methedrine (speed) and ergot alkaloids (ergot is the fungus from which LSD is synthesized). Not one contained a trace of mescaline.

Another natural hallucinogen that is becoming popular among young drug users is psilocybin, the "magic mushroom" from the Mexican plant, *teonanacatl*. Psilocybin is sold on the illicit market in crystal, powder or liquid form. Its mind-altering effects are similar to those of mescaline. Some users claim it gives a more stable, less intense high than LSD. A dose of psilocybin is considerably less potent than an equal amount of LSD. Synthesized in 1958, the man-made form is now being widely used in controlled experiments.

The Aztecs worshipped another Mexican plant, known as *ololuiqui,* for its magical properties. Later identified as the white flowered morning glory, the seeds of this plant contain two of the LSD alkaloids. Recent studies reveal, however, that only two varieties of morning glory seeds, Heavenly Blue and Pearly Gates, possess psychedelic properties. Other varieties of the plant contain poisonous ergot fungus derivatives in dangerously large amounts. In addition, packaged morning glory seeds sold in the United States are often coated with toxic chemicals which will poison the user.

The seeds may be crushed to release the psychoactive substances, chewed or brewed as a tea. Various methods for attempting to extract psychoactive substances from the seeds are offered in "underground" press pamphlets, but these seeds have not achieved widespread popularity. A "trip" or psychedelic experience on Heavenly Blue or Pearly Gates is similar to one on LSD but is usually inconsistent and less intense in its effects.

d-Lysergic acid diethylamide, known as LSD-25 or "acid," is the colorless, odorless, tasteless "turn on," that looks as harmless as water in solution and yet is one of the most potent mind-altering chemicals known to man.

First synthesized at Switzerland's Sandoz laboratories on May 2, 1938, its psychedelic properties were not discovered until 1943, when chemist Dr. Albert Hoffmann accidentally took the first "trip" on LSD. Hoffmann's first experience was relatively mild, consisting of kaleidoscopic color and images. Deducing that he must have absorbed some LSD while working with it, Hoffmann later returned to the laboratory and swallowed 250 micrograms (a powerful dose) of the chemical. This time he experienced a full-blown psychedelic excursion, and the drug became classified for research purposes as a "psychotomimetic" because it was believed to produce a temporary psychosis in the user.

The drug has been generally available in this country since 1962, and although it was outlawed with other hallucinogens in 1966, recent studies indicated that perhaps 1 to 3 percent of all students in the United States have experimented with LSD once. A considerably smaller percentage of these experimenters become chronic users or "acid heads." Surveys of individual college campuses show a higher incidence of LSD use in and around the large universities in the northeast and on the west coast than among the smaller midwestern and southern schools. The highest concentration of use, however, has been among the cults of Greenwich Village in New York and Haight-Ashbury cults in San Francisco, where it now appears to be dropping off.

Most LSD experimenters appear to be middle-class adolescents and young adults who are "turned on" (introduced to the drug) by a friend or a relative. LSD use seems to have spread predominantly among middle- and upper-class intellectual and artistic communities. Relatively little LSD has been discovered in ghettos and poorer neighborhoods.

A semisynthetic substance, LSD is extracted from ergot fungus, a black rust that grows on rye, wheat and other grains. Lysergic acid is the natural component of the ergot alkaloids from which d-lysergic acid diethylamide, also an alkaloid, is synthesized. Using ergot fungus and fairly uncomplicated lab equipment, an amateur chemist can easily reproduce the substance, by far the most powerful of the mind drugs. One ounce will supply about 280,000 doses of 100 mcg. each. After it is swallowed, LSD flows rapidly through the body and disappears from body fluids before the "trip" begins. Greater quantities appear to concentrate in the liver than in the brain.

The exact chemical action of LSD upon the human system is unknown and is still under intensive study. Several theories, however, have been set forth.

Most scientists agree that LSD acts upon many cells, tissues and organs as well as upon the central nervous system. Research indicates that it probably, in some way, affects the transmitting of nerve impulses from one nerve cell to another. In so doing it distorts or exaggerates sense impulses being transmitted to the brain. Further, the impulses transmitted from one sense organ, for example, the eye, are affected by those from another, perhaps the ear. This produces the phenomena known as synesthesia, described often by LSD users who "see" music, "taste" color or "smell" sounds. Increased electrical activity in the brain, heightened sensitivity to what is observed through the sense organs and decreased muscular coordination occur.

There is also the possibility that LSD's major action may be indirect. It may produce major changes in the physical system which controls substances vital to mental functioning.

No deaths have been directly attributed to the drug's impact on the body. However, instances of injury or death following LSD use have been reported, as in the case of students who have crashed to their deaths from upper story windows or wandered in front of oncoming cars on highways. LSD delusions or panic reactions may have been the decisive factor in some or all of these cases. Then again underlying causes may have been responsible.

Common physical effects are raised blood pressure, dilated pupils, trembling, sweating and reddening of the face. A user may also feel cold or numb, or suffer from nausea.

Changes in consciousness usually begin around a half hour after consumption and, for a moderate dose (100 to 200 micrograms), last 9 to 12 hours. If the drug is injected directly into the bloodstream, however, symptoms may appear within minutes.

Psychological changes triggered by LSD, many of which are highly subjective, occur on three distinct levels. Sense perceptions are greatly distorted. Emotional reactions are usually exaggerated, and accustomed thought patterns undergo strange transformations.

The human being maintains his mental grip on the realities of physical existence primarily through his sense perceptions. LSD tends to loosen that grip on the outer world by confusing or blurring the normal sense signals sent to the brain. An LSD user may look at a painting and suddenly see all the colors flow together in a single stream. Colors often seem brighter and objects may appear luminescent as though an inner light were suddenly switched on. Walls may move and window frames tremble. One girl described a wooden floor as a huge brown ocean undulating in slow rhythmic waves. She proceeded to climb the crests of these waves and slide down. Such subjective psychological effects of LSD are as many, as varied and as complex as the individuals who try it. There is, however, a long list of sensations commonly experienced.

LSD tends to undermine a person's emotional stability during an experience. Customary controls over one's emotions may diminish or disappear entirely. Thus a user may suffer sudden swift shifts of mood or have difficulty controlling sudden feelings. Extreme anxiety or panic, severe depression or hysterical laughter may occur. These emotions may stem from the individual's personality or pent-up problems. On the other hand, they may be merely spontaneous and greatly exaggerated reactions to momentary mood changes.

As is the case with sense perception, the barriers between different levels of conscious and subconscious thought appear to be blurred during an LSD experience. This confusing of the normal limits of thinking and awareness is the phenomenon usually described as "consciousness - expansion." An LSD "tripper" may feel divided into two parts: an observing self and an experiencing self. He may feel that his observing, thinking self is off at a distance watching his other self experience the trip. In fact, he may actually see his body as though he were two people—one watching the other.

The mystique of LSD for the curious and the young lies in the surreal world of expanding consciousness, where barriers to new realms of mental experience dissolve. But since the LSD experience is also an unstable and highly subjective experience, underlying stress and strains, insecurity, anxiety as to the effects of the drug, unpleasant surroundings and unexpected noises or events can all plunge a user into panic.

Usually the individual remains well aware that his strange experiences are drug-induced. Occasionally, however, he may become totally immersed in his imaginings and "freak out" (lose all contact with reality). In most cases a user can be "talked down," or guided back to reality with barbiturates if someone is around to do it.

Preoccupation with inner experience, in any case, is usually so intense that the individual's ability to think "realistically" is greatly reduced. This means a decreased capacity to concentrate on and judge the consequences of his actions and those of the people around him. The blurring of mental boundaries inhibits the ability to organize and stabilize perceptions of reality. It can be argued, therefore, that LSD confuses consciousness as much as it expands it.

In certain controlled situations, LSD has produced profound personality insights and greater appreciation of life or God. How long these new outlooks last is uncertain. Some people show marked improvement in adjusting to their lives and problems for six or eight months, then suddenly relapse into old behavior patterns. Others may continue improving. Many claim they have gained new insights but exhibit no proof of these in their actions. Such experiments have almost always been con-

Before   After

When Spiders Take to Drugs ...

Experiments with animals often give scientists valuable clues to the effect of drugs on human beings. Dr. Peter N. Witt, director of research at North Carolina Department of Mental Health, hit upon the idea of using spiders, known for their extraordinary sense of balance and direction, as expressed in the nearly perfect symmetry of the webs they weave. He invited thousands of spiders to a most unusual drug party, supplied them with amphetamines, tranquilizers and barbiturates, and then watched to see how the drugged solution they had sipped from a syringe would affect their nervous and muscular systems.

The result can be seen in the irregular pattern of the webs woven by the spiders. The most "disturbed" patterns were caused by high doses of barbiturates, as shown in these photographs of two webs built by the same adult female cross spider (weight 89.4 mg). The web to the left shows a normal pattern, woven under normal conditions. The one to the right shows what happened two days later, after the spider had been stoned on phenobarbital.

51

ducted by trained psychotherapists on carefully screened individuals. Research into the use of LSD to solve personality problems of alcoholics and the mentally ill is continuing. But at present, scientific debate revolves around the risks of permanent physical and psychological harm. Although there have been more than 2,500 scientific papers published on different aspects of the drug, the answers to the questions: Does LSD break chromosomes? damage the brain? or inflict mental illness? have yet to be established beyond a doubt.

The most surprising for users who were willing to accept the personal risks involved in the exploration of "inner space" was the news that some doctors felt they were simultaneously reducing their chances for producing normal children. According to Dr. Kurt Hirschorn, chief of medical genetics at the Mt. Sinai School of Medicine in New York, very few drugs are as potentially damaging to the chromosomes because LSD, he found, caused not only breakage, but also, like radiation, *rearrangements* of the cells. He interpreted these findings to mean that the user then faced an increased vulnerability to leukemia "and other neoplasms;" the possibility of creating congenital malformations in an unborn child; and the "danger of producing long-lasting genetic damage that goes on into future generations."

Dr. Cheston M. Berlin, a pediatrician at the George Washington University School of Medicine, adds that "although we cannot rush in and say we have unequivocal evidence at this time that LSD use causes birth defects, we are on firmer ground, more suspicious than ever before." In an investigation completed in spring, 1970, Dr. Berlin and his associates found in their experiment that the rate of birth defects in children of LSD users, either father or mother, was eighteen times as high as that of the general population.

Another hazardous aspect of LSD use is the possibility of acute mental side effects. Instances of recurring psychedelic symptoms, long after the actual trip, have been reported. Descriptions of these flashbacks indicate that effects may recur while the individual is high on another drug or in a state of depression or anxiety. The person's susceptibility may be the determining factor, but then it is as yet impossible to know how easily affected an individual will be. People both with and without a prior tendency to mental instability have suffered unpleasant, long-lasting reactions from LSD use.

Dr. Timothy Leary, a major advocate of the drug, whose original research spurred much of the sensationalism attached to its use, has also frequently emphasized that "it is a very powerful drug." He testified in 1966 before a congressional committee that its use should be stringently controlled. His suggestion that "licensing" for its use be as strictly supervised as that for flying airplanes is one measure of the potency with which "acid" is regarded by even its most uncritical supporters.

Debate over the risks and rewards of LSD use will most likely continue until the true nature of its action on the body and brain is discovered. But pending concrete proof of definite harms or benefits resulting from its use, LSD is best described as a powerful chemical, the use of which should be subject to strictest control, caution and common sense.

The same reservations are true regarding the use of LSD's two most popular relatives: DMT (Demethytryptamine) and its analogues; and STP (2,5-dimethoxy-4-methyl-amphetamine). Neither is as popular as LSD among serious hallucinogenic users, but both are usually available to this group. Less powerful than "acid," DMT induces a much more sudden "trip" which is of short duration. This "blast" is usually considered too overwhelming to be of interest to most LSD users. STP is only about one-fiftieth as potent as LSD but, when taken in large amounts, its effects may be similar.

Like the other powerful hallucinogens, there is little possibility that LSD, DMT and STP will ever become broadly accepted even among the most naive users. Reports now from Haight-Ashbury, where the price for LSD has recently dropped from $1.50 to 30¢ a dose, indicate that many of the former "acid" users have turned to other ways of life that have proved more satisfying for them. Dr. Joel Fort contends that many original enthusiasts have discovered that "drugs just don't change reality." Dropping out of the drug world, hundreds in San Francisco have now turned to social activism, or the attempted utopia of country life to achieve a "natural high" for themselves. Frequently, they have also become devotees of yoga or some other Eastern religion.

According to novelist William Burroughs, who lived with drugs for many years, "anything that can be accomplished by chemical means can also be accomplished by other means, given sufficient knowledge of the process involved." For members of the Hindu Meher Baba cult, and others like it, this means a deliberate abstinence from all drugs and the development of rigorous techniques of meditation. One disciple says that with LSD, "your own impurities keep bringing you down," while with meditation, you can recreate the "high" of the acid trip at will and without side-effects. The most famous advocate of this alternative to the drug experience is Dr. Richard Alpert, formerly an associate of Timothy Leary at Harvard, who is now known as Baba Ram Dass.

But whatever their reasoning, there is growing evidence that some of the strongest voices being raised today against the mind drugs belong to those who once trusted them implicitly.

CHAPTER FOUR

The Opiates

Throughout the years, opium, morphine, codeine and heroin, classed collectively as the opiates, have relieved man's physical pain and eased his mental misery. These derivatives of the poppy plant, while serving as valuable pain relievers, also have been among the most socially destructive drugs in existence. Between the Asian opium smoker of 2,000 B.C. and the American heroin addict of 1970, there stretches a long tragic story of misuse and mishandling of these drugs.

The practice of opium smoking existed for thousands of years before man discovered that it possessed undesirable attributes beyond those that left him dreamy, drowsy and forgetful. It was not until the drug invaded European cities in the form of gum opium and laudanum (tincture of opium) that man realized something stronger than a mere desire for "repose" was tying him to the opium habit. Samuel Coleridge, who supposedly wrote the poem *Kubla Khan* under the influence of opium, later called it "an accursed habit, a wretched vice, a species of madness, a derangement, an utter impotence of volition"—in other words, drug *addiction*. Today this condition is understood to be physical dependence upon a drug because the body cells adapt to it or build up tolerance, thus instilling a physical craving which cannot be denied without painful suffering.

This relationship between man and the opiates was not scientifically recognized, however, until after morphine was isolated from opium resin. Called "God's own medicine" by the English surgeon, Sir William Osler, because of its pain-killing properties, the new drug soon became the mainstay of the medical profession. But as more doctors began to depend on it medically, their patients became dependent upon it physically.

In 1848, a new technical invention seemed to provide a safe method of prescribing morphine. The invention was the hypodermic needle. At the time, most experts believed the needle would stop addiction because direct injection prevented the drug from passing through the stomach. Unfortunately the hypodermic syringe greatly heightened the drug's effects (60 milligrams of morphine taken by mouth is less effective in killing pain than 8 milligrams administered through injection), and the availability of both drug and needle helped spread addiction on a "do-it-yourself" basis. The addict no longer had to buy a "prepared medicine." He could purchase everything he needed at the drugstore. By 1898 it was estimated that 1.4 million or 4 percent of the American population was addicted to some form of opium.

In 1874, a German doctor, Heinrich Dreser, discovered another "cure" for morphine addiction. Christened heroin after the Greek god Heros, thereby reflecting hopes that it would be of great benefit to mankind, the new drug was enthusiastically prescribed as a cure for both opium and morphine addiction. A few months later pharmacologists and doctors realized their error. Heroin not only caused addiction; it soon proved to be two and a half times stronger than morphine. And of all drug dependencies, heroin addiction is perhaps the most difficult to cure.

Because of its powerful addicting properties, heroin has been barred from medical use in the United States and is therefore available only through illicit channels. Illegal traffickers keep the price high and the quality low.

As a result, the story of heroin addiction in the United States today is perhaps typified by an ex-addict's description of his experience: "It's a 24-hour-a-day thing. You get up in the morning, you shoot some drugs, and you go out on the street. You commit . . . a crime to get . . . more money. You buy some more drugs. . . . It's a constant thing."

The inner city slum has known this "constant thing" as a debilitating drain on its manpower and its families for over twenty years. Today the rest of America is discovering drug addiction, as heroin spreads from the slums into the suburbs. And in both the inner city and the suburb, heroin is attracting the curiosity of the young. The 1969 Senate hearings on narcotics determined that the average age of the addict is under twenty-one. Twenty years ago it was over thirty. Moreover, from Florida to California there have been reports of fourth graders using heroin.

Drug addiction among teen-age youngsters is not new. But it used to be the older teen-ager who experimented.

As one former heroin addict who now works in a large city rehabilitation center observed, "When I went away in 1963 there was a certain age kids all over this city were using . . . "stuff" (heroin)—18, 19. When I came back (in 1966) the kids were so much younger—15 and 16." In the suburbs the problem of heroin use is much newer. There the average age of the heroin user seems to be somewhere between 15 and 20, mostly high school students seeking a new experience. But in the ghetto the age of the experimenter continues to drop.

In 1969, 12-year-old Walter Vandermeer died in Harlem from a heroin overdose. Eleven-year-olds have been arrested for selling drugs. As one ex-addict in Washington, D.C., described his impressions of the problem today, "In the last six months, it's 11, 12, 13, 14. Boys and girls, you know. Sometimes you think it's a dream when you see kids that age (using drugs)."

The reasons recited for both the affluent and the poor youngster's use of heroin somehow sound the same. One 17-year-old suburban youth—a former addict—described his reasons for turning to heroin:

> I just wasn't doing anything. Life was kind of meaning-
> less, aimless; every day was just there. I wasn't actively
> involved in anything, and I wasn't really enjoying any-
> thing. The way I see it, the people who are into drugs—
> nothing holds their interest and there's no real meaning

for them, so this is what they get to.

The traditional "reasons" why the ghetto youngster begins using heroin are similar—there is nothing to hold his interest, nothing to aim for, so he turns to heroin for escape, plus a thrill.

Similarly, the desire for a "kick" is propelling both ghetto and suburban youths toward heroin. One New York youth observed that "the kids are mostly looking for adventure. . . . They got most of what they want and they're looking for something else."

A 23-year-old ex-addict from an urban slum sounded the same theme. "It's just this thing, they hear about these groovy highs and they want to experiment." But as one young ex-addict observed, "It seems . . . as if there's just something in heroin, something that gets in your veins the first time you do it, and even if it's not a physical addiction, there's just a calling that's in you once you do it."

"I thought I could beat it." . . . "I didn't think I'd get hooked." . . . "I thought I could handle it." Every addict once thought that he was "different," that he could have the high without the hell. Thus ex-addicts have only one kind of advice for the young: *"Don't start. Heroin may be dynamite stuff, but you can't beat it. Nobody beats it. Horse is king and you'll end up its slave."*

Stuff, dope, horse, smack: heroin has many names on the street. Today it is called the king of the "cop-outs." Yesterday it was the monkey on your back. But no matter what the epithet, the drug remains the master and the addict must serve.

What is it that heroin offers the addict? What makes him risk addiction, disease from dirty needles, death from poisoned drugs and degrading prison sentences?

When it is "mainlined" (injected directly in the vein), heroin immediately produces a feeling of exhilaration known as a "rush." This is accompanied by an intense tingling thrill that shivers the stomach. When the initial elation wears off, the addict begins to "nod out," a condition caused by the narcotic effect of the drug which dims sense perception and produces lethargy and drowsiness. This tranquil pleasant state, which really makes the effect of heroin a "low" not a "high," lasts several hours in the beginning. As the body develops tolerance, however, the addict must inject the drug, or "fix," more frequently. He soon needs a new "fix" or shot every few hours, and as the time between shots decreases, the amount needed increases.

Most addicts, however, begin by sniffing heroin rather than "mainlining" it. Sniffing is the easiest method of taking the drug since the user merely dumps the powder in a paper bag or puts a little on a match cover and sniffs. Many, especially teen-agers who remain in school, continue sniffing the drug in order to avoid identifying needle-marks or to prevent themselves from getting heavily hooked. This practice may work for a while, but the user eventually notices that he is not getting the same "kick" or that he needs to take the drug two or three times as often. Moreover, sudden death can result from sniffing heroin as easily as from injecting an overdose. Addicts have died within seconds after snorting heroin mixed with lye or some other alkaline substance.

Most steady users will progress to injecting the drug in order to satisfy their physical craving or to get a more intense "rush." Skin-popping (injecting the drug just under the skin, but not into a vein) is usually the first step, but many addicts claim it takes too long to feel the results—perhaps 3 to 5 minutes. Thus, sooner or later, most addicts begin to mainline.

Heroin has to be "cooked" before it can be injected. The usual procedure is to put some water and some heroin in a spoon, a bottle cap or any other small metal container. The addict lights a match under it and cooks the mixure until the heroin dissolves. He then draws the solution into a hypodermic syringe and injects the drug into a vein.

The procedure of mainlining often has an air of ritual about it. After tying a belt or scarf around his arm to make the blood vessels stand out, the addict begins to probe for the vein. Sometimes he jabs the needle into his skin several times before hitting his mark. When he finally punctures the vein, the addict may draw some blood up into the syringe, often watching it mix with the heroin. Then he injects some of the solution and withdraws the needle.

One young addict explained that he only injected half the drug at a time because "If you put it all in at once, you might take an overdose. You put half in and see how it feels; then you see if you can take the other half."

One theme that seems to dominate when ex-addicts recall their experience is how sloppy they were. One 17-year-old youth from a Maryland suburb recalled that he started with a resolution that he would use a new needle every time. Yet he finally resorted to "picking up a cup out of a gas station and getting some water out of a spigot. . . . I tore an empty soft drink can in half and cooked it in the top of that. But it seems as if that happens to everybody who does it. That's one thing I think makes this drug so much different, how it lowers you."

Another ex-addict, 26-year-old Pernell Smith, who works for a Washington, D.C., treatment center, described his impressions of addicts:

> They'll shoot dope anywhere they can get it—an abandoned house, an old car. They'll use a dirty spike (rusty needle)—anything to get the drug in the vein. If they don't have a spike, they'll bum one from someone else. It doesn't matter if it's rusty. And they know what dirty spikes can do. A rusty needle—it'll pull the skin in and soon there's an abscess. They may lose an arm or a hand because the skin rots away. But it just doesn't seem to matter.

The usual picture of an addict mainlining shows him sticking a needle into a bulging vein in his arm. Many addicts, however, must resort to other parts of the body. Smith says:

> Some people have deep veins. They may try coke needles (long needles used for shooting cocaine), but if that doesn't work they'll shoot some place else. The same thing happens to guys who use it for a long time. Their veins sink down and they can't hit them. I've seen guys take an hour or more trying to hit a vein, some so frustrated they start crying. But once the arm veins are gone they'll shoot some place else. Where? In the neck, the

legs, under the fingernail—the hands usually.

"Tracks" or needle-marks are the traditional identifying mark of a heroin addict. Craters—abscesses surrounded by rotting skin—are another frequent result, usually the result of using rusty needles. Increasingly puffed hands, often swollen to twice the normal size from prolonged shooting into the back of the hand, identify the heavy addict.

The addict courts another danger every time he sticks a needle into his arm—that of infection. He stands an excellent chance of contracting hepatitis at least once. Also many doctors say heroin addicts are bringing back tetanus, a disease which was once completely under control. Dirty needles inflict abscesses which attract the tetanus bacteria.

The pain of withdrawal, however, is the most frequently experienced and one of the most dreaded consequences of heroin addiction. The desire to avoid this suffering is one of the main reasons an addict continues to seek his drug, even in the face of possible death or disease. For if an addict is denied heroin, physical symptoms, which are probably due to tolerance (the body's cellular adaptation to the drug), appear. These symptoms are known as physical withdrawal, which is often described as being much like "a severe case of flu."

The following is a typical description of "kicking the habit" as told by a young woman who withdrew "cold turkey"— that is, without medication:

> It's like a terrible case of the flu. Your joints move involuntarily—that's where the phrase "kick the habit" comes from. You jerk and twitch and you just can't control it; you throw up; you can't control your bowels either, and this goes on for four or five days. And afterwards, for 15 days afterwards, you can't sleep and you're gagging all the time and you cough up blood because if you're on drugs, you don't eat and that's all there is to cough up.

Rescuing drug addicts from heroin's grip has recently become a booming activity. Dozens of rival theories and rehabilitation methods are flooding the "market," each vying for federal funds. Perhaps none provides the ultimate solution, but they are a welcome change after years of neglect and apathy. These treatment programs range from utopian communities like Synanon to the methadone maintenance plan of Drs. Nyswander and Dole, which replaces heroin with another drug.

Synanon, perhaps the most original of the "therapeutic communities," operates on the theory that the addict mentally is still a child. Founded by Chuck Dederich in Santa Monica, California, it has expanded operations across the nation, setting up Synanon houses in several major cities.

Synanon claims not to be in the "rehabilitation industry" as much as in the "utopian-society business." Every addict who applies is a potential member for life. Instead of preparing the addict to return to the streets, permanent communities are organized where he may remain if he chooses. Synanon accepts private donations and secures the rest of its income through various enterprises it owns and operates.

Dederich expresses the belief that addicted people should not be blamed for their acts nor treated like criminals. Instead, he argues, they are adults who have not grown up. Like children, they are without a sense of responsibility, without a conscience.

In his Synanon project, Dederich explains, he is trying to "create an extended family . . . (with) a strong almost autocratic father-figure, who dispenses firm justice combined with warm concern, who is a model extolling inner-directed convictions about the old fashioned virtues of honesty, sobriety, education and hard work."

Daytop Village in New York City is an outgrowth of the Synanon concept. The Daytop program, however, prepares the addict for reentry into society. Founded by David Deitch, a Synanon graduate, it also treats the addict as though he were a child who demands everything and offers nothing. Ex-"street junkies" (addicts) are used, as well as professional therapists, to break through this selfish shell and instill a working sense of love and loyalty in the addict. The Daytop program for rehabilitating the addict may take from one to three years. It has made some impact on the general public through theatrical dramatizations of the drug problem, produced and performed by Daytop members.

The Odyssey House theory, developed by Dr. Judianne Densen-Gerber, also promotes the psycho-therapeutic setting. It began as a pilot research program at New York's Metropolitan Hospital in 1966. Odyssey House, Inc., was opened in 1967, operated by seventeen ex-addicts and three professional psychiatrists. Today it houses seventy residents. The central belief of this voluntary agency is that ex-addicts can function without drugs and that they have a responsibility to prevent the spread or continuation of addiction in the community. Thus addicts who are members of Odyssey House attempt to set an example for other addicts and help educate the community in the dangers of drug addiction.

An essential part of the treatment is the follow-up procedure designed to help the addict after he has returned to the community. Odyssey House helps him to find a job or get into school before he leaves the program. Six months later his departure is recommended if he has shown sufficient progress. The only requirements for "graduates" of the program are two group therapy sessions each week, which are led by a doctor trained in the techniques of Odyssey House.

The methadone maintenance plan operates on a totally different concept. It is a medical, not a psychiatric treatment and is designed to reach the hundreds of addicts who cannot be accommodated by the presently limited intensive care facilities. The program was developed by Dr. Vincent Dole, of the Rockefeller Institute, and his wife, Dr. Marie Nyswander. According to research conducted by Dr. Dole, heroin addiction may cause permanent metabolic changes in the body. Therefore, he considers drug addiction a disease which requires continuing medication.

The medication Dr. Dole advocates is methadone, a synthetic narcotic. Methadone is also addictive, but when taken by mouth, it causes no euphoria or high. In small doses it merely extinguishes the addict's craving for heroin. Larger doses will also block the "high" caused by heroin even if the patient mainlines it. Patients need to take only one, relatively small dose of the colorless liquid daily.

The Nyswander-Dole program requires only that the individual leave a urine specimen each time he picks up his supply of methadone. (This may be daily or in later stages, weekly.)

As of the fall of 1969, the Nyswander-Dole program in New York City had enrolled over 2,000 addicts. Only 18 percent had dropped out. At least 95 percent of those still in the program were in school or held jobs.

Unfortunately, except for the mass methadone plan, which is now being operated in several cities, most private and federally sponsored treatment programs are extremely costly and touch only a small portion of the nation's heroin addicts. President Nixon, speaking at a White House Drug Conference in October 1969, said there were 180,000 addicts in this country. Other official estimates based only on *known,* registered addicts, place the number as low as 30,000.

The Bureau of Narcotics and Dangerous Drugs listed 28,128 drug addicts for New York City in February 1969. The New York Medical Examiner, however, estimates that the total number of heroin addicts in New York is closer to 100,000. Of these he believes 25,000 may be under twenty-one. These estimates are based on the fact that only 1 percent of those who die from narcotics overdose each year are registered addicts. In 1969 close to 1,000 died.

The figures for other major cities show much the same discrepancies. In Washington, D.C., 1,395 are registered, but Dr. Robert L. DuPont, Director of that city's Narcotics Treatment Agency, estimates that there may be between 5,000 and 15,000 addicts in the nation's capital. San Francisco lists only 609 addicts, yet a Stanford psychiatrist who has studied the problem says there are between 2,000 and 9,000 heroin addicts in the former "flower-child" district of Haight-Ashbury alone. Most experts agree that probably half of the nation's addicts live in New York City. If the total there is 100,000, the country's entire addicted population may well be about 200,000.

Most of these addicts cannot afford their habit. Someone supporting a 30 cap (capsule) "habit" must spend $50 a day on heroin. Other addicts need as many as 100 shots a day. It may cost these individuals from $100 to $200 a day merely to stave off withdrawal. The average cost of a "moderate" habit is $30 to $50 daily.

There is no way for the majority of these addicts to support their habits except by stealing or dealing (selling heroin). Furthermore, to get the money for a $50 habit an addict must steal goods worth five times that amount—in other words, $250 a day—because they must sell stolen articles at a fraction of their value.

If the estimated national total of 200,000 addicts spent or stole only an average of $20 a day, the total drain on the nation's economy would be $4,000,000 daily. This means almost $1.5 billion annually. Other estimates put the total much higher—close to $5 billion.

Shop-lifting is the most common method by which addicts support their habits. Many sell their stolen goods to respectable citizens. Some have regular customers for suits and color television sets. Other addicts specialize in breaking into apartments or houses to get radios, television sets and other appliances. Women often work as prostitutes or sell heroin for their pushers.

The methods by which younger addicts supply their habit differ somewhat. Many of the wealthier youngsters steal from their parents or forge bad checks. Some families even support their teen-age addicts to keep them from turning to crime. One 20-year-old girl explained that she and her boyfriend lived off a $300 a week payment that his father gave them to supply their habits. She remarked:

"He figures he'd rather support us than have us get busted (arrested). It's not enough, but it sure helps."

Other teen-agers resort to dealing in heroin. This is especially a problem in inner city schools. The pusher is often a young girl who either works alone or with a boy who bargains with customers while she carries the drugs.

School officials say it is almost impossible to convince these teen-age pushers to give up their lucrative business. Many earn as much as $200 a day. Since they can afford expensive clothes as well as a heroin habit, they see nothing wrong with selling narcotics.

This problem of heroin being sold to the young by the young has also penetrated to the suburbs. For instance, reports from

Maryland and Virginia communities bordering on Washington, D.C., indicate that teen-agers can pick up heroin at the neighborhood drive-in along with their hamburgers and cokes.

Contradictory opinions about the spread of heroin from city to suburb appear at every level. Dr. Donald Louria, President of the New York State Council on Drug Addiction, said that "every high school and every college in the country will be inundated by heroin" in a few years. And indeed, heroin is admitted to be a problem in the high schools of many major cities and some suburban areas. However, St. Louis school officials report that they see no evidence of extensive drug use among students. One San Francisco official estimates that perhaps 5 percent of that city's high school students have tried heroin, but that most are not addicted to it. On the other hand, Dr. Leon Wurmser, head of the Drug Abuse Center in Baltimore, claims they are treating a "very substantial number" of people between the ages of 15 and 19.

Another view of the nationwide problem of youthful addiction comes from Chicago, which reports no great increase in the number of young addicts. Dr. Jerome Jaffe, Director of the State Drug Abuse Program in Illinois, stated that "It usually hits either the East or West coast first and then the Midwest. I think we should be cautious."

Heroin addiction among college students is another story. Most university officials strongly doubt that heroin will gain much popularity on the college campus.

Dr. Helen Nowlis, author of Drugs on the College Campus, feels that the great majority of college students understand heroin and don't want anything to do with it.

Surveys at several colleges tend to substantiate this opinion.

Professor Samuel Pearlman conducted a study on drug use among 12,000 university students in New York City. His findings indicate that there has been a slight rise in heroin use but not an increase that he considers significant. He puts the percentage of heroin users at 3 to 4 percent. A year ago it was about 1.5 percent.

A 1968 survey conducted among undergraduates at Rutgers revealed that only 2 percent of those questioned had ever used heroin or any opium derivative. At City College in New York,

1,200 students were questioned. Only 0.72 percent admitted to regular use of narcotics. However, 4.5 percent admitted to one or a few experiences with heroin and other narcotics.

Most available statistics indicate that steady use of heroin on campuses is neither widespread nor popular. Precise information about the extent of heroin use by college students is difficult to gather, however, since the possession of these drugs is illegal. Many students are wary of official surveys and thus may refuse to admit using hard drugs.

Heroin appears to be hitting the man on the job as well as the student. This problem has not reached "crisis" proportions, but many large corporations report a significant loss of employees due to narcotics use.

The situation seems to be the most serious in New York City. An official of the Metropolitan Life Insurance Company says that "more than 100 and less than 1,000 have been fired in the past twelve months." Many of these employees were dismissed because they were actually using drugs at work.

At the New York Telephone Company, a plainclothes agent discovered a heroin ring operating out of the men's room. The company dismissed at least fifty employees during the past year because of narcotics use.

An ex-addict who works at Samaritan Village, a New York rehabilitation center, estimates that about 70 percent of the young people they treat work on Wall Street.

The Laboratory for Chromatography was opened recently to test urine samples from New York firms. Their statistics reveal that 15 percent of the more than 100 tests conducted daily show illicit drug use.

Many corporate officials feel that heroin poses a potentially greater problem than alcoholism. The vice president for personnel of New York Telephone Company admits that "alcoholism still affects a larger segment of our employment, but alcoholism is more easily contained and cured." Heroin, on the other hand, seriously impairs the employee's work performance.

However, Dr. Robert C. Peterson, Director of the National Institute of Mental Health's Center for Studies of Narcotics and Drug Abuse, found the industry problem most unusual.

He expressed the opinion that: "The use of hard drugs in industry is extremely uncommon. It's pretty difficult to maintain employment while on heroin unless you have unlimited funds."

On the job or off, in the school, or on the street, heroin addiction presents a problem of growing magnitude—one which demands greater attention and resources than are presently being applied to it.

CHAPTER FIVE

The Drug Peddlers

In midafternoon, far uptown in New York City's Harlem ghetto, a young black man, barely post-teen, walks west up a tenement-lined street and stops where the corner meets Lenox Avenue. He puts his hands in his pockets, looks about, nods his head and waits. Another man, older, ambles to the corner, then pauses and asks for a light. A box of matches, with a five-dollar bill inside, passes from the young man to the older man. The bill comes out, the older man lights his cigarette and passes the box back after inserting a small glassine envelope, stapled shut, containing a minute quantity of fluffy white powder. The young man lingers a bit, then walks, trots, runs back down the street to his apartment. He locks the door, quickly empties the tiny bag into a spoon and lights a match beneath it. The powder turns brown, bubbles and becomes liquid. The young man sucks the liquid into a syringe and plunges its needle into his forearm. And for five or six hours he is free of the agony of life; his sense perceptions are gone.

Scenes of this kind are not limited to Harlem. The heroin sale could have been made to a middle-class white youth sitting in his car in a suburban roadhouse parking lot in Oak Park, Illinois, or just off a California campus. Users of heroin are rich and poor, black and white, urban and rural. They use drugs as escape from the depression of their lives or to seek new physical sensations.

Heroin has been called the most democratic of substances because its users, whatever their stations, crave it equally. It is not a "social" drug such as marihuana. It enslaves. And because it makes its consumers so dependent, it has an ever-increasing market. It has been estimated that there are perhaps 200,000 drug addicts in this country, about half of them in New York, with thousands of pushers eager to supply them with temporary satisfaction three, four, five times each day. Drug sales, except where carefully regulated by law, are illegal yet there seems to be a limitless supply. Why? How do pushers get those little glassine packets of processed heroin, called "horse" or "smak?" How does an estimated one and a half tons of heroin make its way into the United States annually, involving a trade that amounts to more than $300 million each year?

Heroin, like morphine, is chemically derived from opium, which oozes from the poppy, a flower of heady incense, that blooms in profusion in the Middle Eastern and European countries of Turkey, Iran, India, Bulgaria, Greece, Russia and Yugoslavia; and in the Far East, in Thailand, Burma, Laos and in the Yunan Province of Mainland China. How the brownish seepage from the four-foot tall poppy, flowering on a Middle Eastern mountain farm, becomes processed heroin which is passed clandestinely from seller to user 4,000 miles away on a New York street corner is fairly well known to the Justice Department's Bureau of Narcotics and Dangerous Drugs; to Interpol, the agency through which police of many countries cooperate; to the United Nations Commission on Narcotics; and to undercover agents of many nations. They know the route from farm to arm because at various times and in various places they have uncovered parts of these routes. Never, however, have they been able to follow heroin from its beginnings to its end. Let us see why.

It begins, perhaps, in Afyon Province in Turkey, near the Turkish-Syrian border. More than a half million people live in Afyon, 80 percent of them farmers. They raise wheat, barley, some vegetables—and opium. They raise it legally, under government monopoly which supervises the crop and pays a standard price for it. Turkey ships its opium to various countries, including the United States, for medical use. From the pods of the poppy comes morphine—and the poppy seeds used on rolls all over the world. The poppy is a most useful flower. It generally is agreed that many of the farmers in Afyon do not report their entire crop to the government. They retain hidden bags of opium balls, available for sale to independent buyers.

The chain begins with a buyer, most likely a resident of Afyon, who knows the farmers and who has a reputation for paying more for opium than the government monopoly. He has received, through a friend, an order for 200 kilos (440 pounds) of opium. For several weeks he roams the farmlands, picking up several pounds here, a cache there, paying about $20 a kilo or just under $10 a pound. For his effort he receives a $44 commission, or two Turkish liras per kilo, from the buyer, who takes delivery across the Syrian border. An armed patrol, on hand to fight off border police should there be an encounter, gets $1 per man to escort the 200 kilos over the border, across a three-mile no-man's land studded with antipersonnel mines. The man from Afyon knows the buyer and that is all. The buyer knows the escort, who will get a $25 fee, but that link in the chain ends there. The man in Afyon does not know anything at all about the escort.

The buyer is now in Syria, his escort is back in Turkey. In Azaz, he awaits the next link in the chain, a chemist. This man, using a huge caldron under an open sky, boils the opium with water and lime and ammonium chloride, filters it and arrives at crude morphine, or, as it is called, morphine base. The brownish crystals are placed in waxed paper bags. The weight now is one-tenth of what it was, the 440 pounds of opium are now 44 pounds or 20 kilos, easily hidden in an oil drum on the back of a truck bound for Damascus. The chemist, from nearby Aleppo, receives $5 per kilo of morphine base he extracts—$100—and goes home content.

The truck is parked on a prearranged street in Damascus by the Turkish buyer and is picked up by an Armenian from Beirut, who with a corrupt border guard drives to Beirut, Lebanon. A week later, while drinking tea in a cafe, the buyer receives his $200 commission from someone he has never seen before. He has no idea where the morphine base is, nor does he know who actually placed the order with him. The border guard receives $100 for driving the truck with stolen plates from Damascus, through the border crossing to Beirut, then jumping out of the car to let the Armenian drive to a non-trafficked street in the heart of the Nahr district of Beirut, the Armenian ghetto.

The driver walks away from the truck not even turning his head. Had he done so, he would have seen two men carry the oil drum into a small shop. But that was not his concern. His interest was the $1,000 he would receive, via a deposit in his numbered bank account, a week later. The opium in bags are placed in suitcases within minutes of their removal from the oil drum, and the two men stroll to the waterfront.

A rowboat slips out into Beirut harbor heading toward a French freighter at rest. The blinking of a flashlight guides the boat. It comes to rest amidships. The greyness of the hull is broken as a hatch is opened about 15 feet above the water line. A rope is lowered, with two suitcases tied to one end. The line is tugged, then raised. The rowboat heads back to Beirut. Aboard the freighter an assistant cook takes the packets of morphine base from the cases and throws them into a potato sack among other sacks of potatoes in a galley food locker. Two days later the freighter sails for Marseilles.

Upon docking, the assistant cook does not even look at the precious sack of potatoes. He walks down the ship's gangplank, submits to the necessary customs search and leaves the pier. He makes a phone call from a waterfront bar, saying only, "I'm home." A seaman, who lives aboard the freighter, meanwhile carries the potato sack to his cabin, opens it and takes out the four paper-wrapped packages containing the morphine base. He puts one in his seaman's bag, walks down the gangplank, looks carefully around, then strolls to a pile of lumber next to a fence surrounding the pier area and deposits the sack. He repeats this trip three times, returns to his cabin and waits. Exactly at midnight he leaves the ship again and waits at the lumber pile. In less than a minute a car pulls alongside the fence. The seaman turns the sacks over to a Corsican, who puts them in the trunk of the car. The car drives off.

The opium from Afyon has now safely arrived, as crude morphine, in Marseilles.

The Corsican heads through the center of Marseilles, skirting the heavily policed Opera District. He drives into a quiet residential district, into a narrow street made up of limestone-fronted houses. He parks the car, a rented Citroen, locks the doors and calmly walks away. An hour later, he passes the car keys to another man while they are sharing wine and cheese in a small restaurant.

The following morning, on an estate about twenty miles east of Marseilles, an elegantly dressed gentleman slides into the front seat of his Porsche sports car as his servant places his two expensive suitcases on the rear seat. He tells his servant to inform his wife when she awakes that he is off to Lyons for four or five days. He drives toward the northbound expressway, frequently checking his rearview mirror. There are no followers. After a short distance, he turns onto a dirt road leading to another estate, smaller and less elegant than his, but still impressive. In the basement of this second villa, which he also owns, is a modern, completely equipped laboratory, where he applies his talent as a chemist to converting morphine base into 90 percent pure powdered heroin.

The 20 kilos of morphine in the suitcases are emptied into enamel basins and mixed with acetone, which serves to remove impurities still present, despite the initial boiling in the Syrian hills, and to separate the morphine from opium's other alkaloids. The relatively pure morphine is then filtered, and the chemist is ready to produce heroin. The morphine is boiled with a common laboratory-type acid called acetic anhydride, the vapors passing through glass tubing so that condensation can take place. After six hours of constant boiling, the excess acid is distilled off and the morphine is converted to heroin, impure because of the acetate and salts still in it, but heroin nevertheless. The next step is to wash the impure heroin with water and bone black, which purifies and removes the color from the heroin. It is again filtered, dried and sifted, taking the form of white crystals. The purification process is repeated and the chemist now has 90 percent pure heroin—fine, fluffy white powder, in appearance not unlike baby's talc.

The chemist's fee is $700 a kilo. For converting 20 kilos, he receives $14,000. His money, too, is deposited in a numbered bank account.

The heroin is then packed into double plastic bags, sealed with scotch tape and placed in a metal canister. The next morning it is removed by other anonymous hands. Several days later an exchange student enroute to the United States is offered a $200 commission to deliver a new French sports car to a person who would meet him at the pier when his passenger ship docked in New York. All he must do is to turn over the keys and the registration.

When the liner docks in New York the student waits to be checked through customs with the car registered in his name. He acts innocently and gives rise to no suspicion because he is unaware of his role. He knows nothing of the metal canister sitting beneath a welded piece of metal inside the well holding the sports car's retractable convertible top. The inspection over, he drives the car off the pier and is signalled by the man he was to meet. The man takes the wheel, drops the student in front of a midtown hotel and speeds on until he reaches a private garage in the Bronx. There he and his associates pry the welded seam apart and remove the canister. Inside are forty clear double plastic bags, each containing half a kilogram or just over a pound, of chemically pure heroin. The bags, in two suitcases, are delivered to a furnished room in Brooklyn, where a wholesaler is now ready to do business. One phone call closes the deal. The buyer wants the entire shipment of twenty kilos and will pay, on delivery, $13,000 per kilo.

The next day the wholesaler goes shopping at a supermarket. He carries his groceries home, empties the bags, puts a dozen paper-wrapped plastic envelopes into them and covers the envelopes with the groceries. Later in the day, the bags are delivered to a Manhattan apartment, and shortly afterward two men meet in Central Park. One gives the other a manila envelope. This procedure is repeated over a two-week period until all the heroin is delivered and paid for with $260,000 in used and new bills of various denominations. In a private booth of a foreign currency exchange, the wholesaler counts off his commission of $60,000 and deposits the remaining $200,000 into a numbered account—one that will be drawn upon later by a Corsican in Marseilles.

The heroin is taken by car to a quiet split-level house on Long Island, occupied by an elderly man and his wife. The man is thought by the neighbors to be a retired butcher. He is also an expert at adulterating heroin. He removes some pure heroin from each plastic bag and replaces it with milk sugar. The heroin thus becomes about 75-percent pure and the twenty kilos become twenty-five kilos. The next stop is another mixing laboratory, where one kilo of mannite—a fluffy white children's laxative—is added for every three kilos. There are now thirty-three kilos of heroin, about 55-percent pure. The buyer who purchased twenty kilos of relatively pure heroin for $13,000 a kilo now has thirty-three kilos ready to sell to Harlem distributors at $20,000 a kilo.

One such dealer, a Harlem tough, handles a kilo a week. His "laboratory" is a length of oilcloth spread over a bed in a back room of a 125th Street walkup. He empties his kilo on the cloth. To the 2.2 pounds of 55-percent heroin he adds two pounds of quinine and sixteen pounds of mannite. Through a common kitchen sifter the powders are combined and recombined until there is a twenty-pound white mound piled in the middle of the oilcloth. Then measured spoonsful go into glassine envelopes and by the time the mound disappears there are 2,500 bags of "smak." The Harlem distributor's cost for the heroin, the mannite, the quinine and the help he needs in packaging come to $21,000 a week. For each of his 2,500 bags of horse he gets $25. Deducting commissions to street peddlers and expenses from his total of $62,500, he earns a clear profit of $30,000 a week. The peddlers in turn sell packets at $25 or break them down still further into $5 envelopes.

The 200 kilos of raw opium that cost $4,000 in Afyon several months earlier now has a street-market value, as adulterated heroin "fixes," of more than $2 million. All along the route from Turkey to the United States, money has changed hands and bought complicity and therefore silence. Each link in the chain knows only his particular attachment at either end. That is how the big dealers in drugs—first the Mafia and now the upcoming Spanish-speaking "Mafia"—want it and plan it, and why the work of federal and international narcotics agents is not only dangerous but also tedious and frustrating.

At least 80 percent of the world's illegal heroin originates as Turkish opium. Turkey's neighbor, Iran, used to be as great a source, but in 1955, the Iranian government, frightened by an addiction rate within its borders that was said to be as high as 2 million addicts, banned it completely. Today, Iran has reinstituted the lucrative crop of "legal" opium in what officials call "self defense" against their neighbor, Turkey, despite protestations by the United Nations.

In addition to the Middle Eastern crop, hundreds of tons of illegal opium is grown annually by the hill tribes of Thailand. As with the farmers of Afyon, opium brings them illegal money, but not much of it. The opium moves across the Thai-Burmese border and, as raw opium, morphine base or crude heroin, finds its way to northern Thai cities and on to Bangkok for distribution throughout Asia and the United States. Chinese Nationalist smugglers and Thai traders buy from the farmers and, using humans as pack carriers, then boats, buses, Land Rovers and trains, move the cargo to the China Sea. Narcotics authorities agree generally that opium grown in Communist China is consumed internally, in Hong Kong and Taiwan. However, the amount that reaches the United States is believed to be only about 5 percent of the total sold here.

While pressure is maintained on Iran to outlaw its opium production again, an Agency for International Development loan of $3 million to help Turkey develop alternate crops raises some hope of reducing the opium supply. Prior to June 30, 1967, 21 Turkish provinces, including Afyon, were authorized to grow opium poppies. This number was reduced to 18, then last year to 11, and by 1971 it is hoped there will be only five provinces legally growing opium.

Since Turkish farmers receive only about $8 million a year for their crop, it has also been suggested that the entire crop be purchased outright each year by the United States.

John Ingersoll, director of the Bureau of Narcotics and Dangerous Drugs, says: "Hopefully, the Government of Turkey will be in a position to eliminate opium poppy production in 1972.

This would have a profound effect on the smuggling of heroin into the United States as well as stabilizing national narcotics production in the Middle and Near East." Ironically, war in the Middle East has also disrupted many of the old trade routes, and the overland passage through Communist countries is much riskier for smugglers.

A good deal of heroin comes into the country from Canada, where border inspection is perfunctory, and from Mexico. However, the major importation from the South is of marihuana. Recent statistics showed that two American-Mexican border efforts, "Operation Intercept" and "Operation Cooperation," produced this harvest in a month-and-a-half-period from September 21 to November 7, 1969: 8,000 pounds of marihuana; 80 pounds of hashish; 223 seizures of amphetamines and barbiturates; and 34 seizures of heroin in varying amounts.

The traffic in marihuana which consists of the leaves and hashish which is the solid yellow resin of the cannabis plant, is wider than that of heroin, but the routes into the United States are diffuse and less organized and thus even less easily traced. There appears to be a good deal more "amateur" importation, perhaps because less money is involved. Most captures of marihuana and hashish—large or small—occur either by accident, during concerted drives such as "Operation Intercept" and "Operation Cooperation," or during spasmodic crackdowns by federal and local law enforcement officials. The news reports provide many examples:

Five men and two women arrested in Long Beach while floating 900 pounds of marihuana up from Mexico along the California coastline in a salvage barge; a woman skier, stopped at the Canadian border, her purse filled with marihuana; the son of the Governor of New Jersey charged with possession of the drug; a party of scientists from Pasadena's Jet Propulsion Laboratory raided, with hashish and marihuana confiscated; the son of a New York banker arrested trying to smuggle hashish into the country inside a scuba tank; the son of a former candidate for Governor of New York arraigned for possession of hashish; 600 pounds of hashish found by Boston customs inspectors in false bottoms of crates of musical instruments from India.

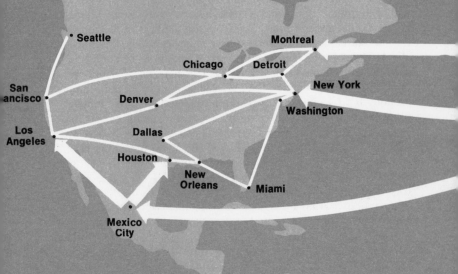

Drug Routes to the U.S.

Seattle
Montreal
Chicago
Detroit
San ancisco
Denver
New York
Washington
Los Angeles
Dallas
Houston
New Orleans
Miami
Mexico City

Marihuana and hashish come into this country packed in automobile doors and underneath seat cushions. The drug turns up in plastic bags in fraternity houses and on the streets. More often than not it is brought back as a "favor" and distributed socially, often without charge. Soldiers in Vietnam can buy it openly, for pennies, on any street corner in Saigon, and efforts by U.S. military authorities to snuff out its use have resulted only in arrests that do not seem to deter usage.

It has been estimated by the House of Representatives Select

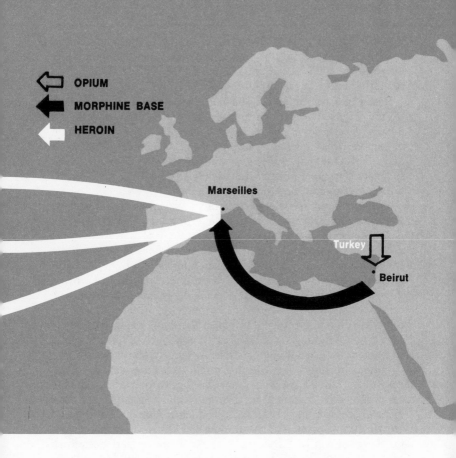

OPIUM
MORPHINE BASE
HEROIN

Marseilles

Turkey

Beirut

Committee on Crime that 250 million people around the world have used marihuana or hashish; that as many as 12 million Americans have tried marihuana; that 15 million people say that someone close to them uses it; that regular users in this country total 3 million; that as many as 31 percent of teen-agers may be users. The Committee estimates that expenditure for cannabis use comes to $850 million. Though the figure is debatable, it indicates the extent of the traffic and use of the drug. Most of the marihuana smuggled into this country comes from

Mexico—as much as 95 percent, according to the Federal Bureau of Narcotics and Dangerous Drugs. Small amounts are also grown, wild or cultivated, across the United States, particularly in the American Southwest.

Recently a computerized "suspect bank" has been made part of the Mexican-American border antimarihuana program. It details descriptions, arrest records and methods of operation of known or suspected smugglers. It is expected to cut down delays of innocent tourists at the border, while pinpointing suspects. Another successful device has been the use of trained police dogs to sniff out concealed supplies of the drug.

While the public debates just how dangerous marihuana is, traffic in this drug remains a serious problem. If a person believes marihuana is a necessary ingredient of admission to a certain intellectual or social set, then he does not regard its transportation as a criminal act, laws to the contrary notwithstanding. If users believe that alcohol is equally as harmful, then a rationale for marihuana smoking is created. While the controversy over the nature of marihuana continues, total compliance with antimarihuana laws can hardly be expected.

Because smoking "pot" has acquired such a broad social character, its casual importation and even more casual distribution are not adaptable to formal "trade routes" as in the case of heroin. Those who favor the legalization of marihuana or progressive leniency in dealing with offenders fear that more repressive measures will produce a stratified system of growth, transportation, importation and distribution controlled by the underworld. They point to American experiences with prohibition and to the traffic in heroin. These advocates favor research and education over layers of laws.

On the other hand, the solution to the ever-increasing traffic in stimulant and depressive pills may lie in more stringent laws governing their manufacture and distribution. According to a recent survey by the Bureau of Narcotics and Dangerous Drugs, U.S. drug companies legitimately manufacture 92 percent of the "up and down" pills in illicit traffic—pills which can become addictive if used regularly and in large quantities, and which are more available than either marihuana or heroin.

Last year the House Select Committee on Crime, attempting

to determine the routes by which amphetamines leave and re-enter this country, uncovered a pattern of ineffective federal regulation, corporate negligence, and complicity on the part of some of the smaller drug firms that profit from illegal trade.

An estimated 8 billion amphetamine pills are produced each year in this country, most of them pills to relieve weariness, to keep one awake, or to assist in weight reduction. Federal officials estimate that no more than half of this production is routinely dispensed through doctors' prescriptions. The remainder is diverted to criminal channels by dishonest employees of manufacturers and wholesalers, by pilfering, by hijacking of trucks. Then there is the doctor who may carelessly overprescribe and pharmacist who may tend to refill prescriptions repeatedly without represcription.

Government investigators say that many drug companies make little effort to verify the legitimacy of customers who order amphetamines. To prove this they set up a fictitious company in the Midwest and received without question nearly every drug ordered from manufacturers. Sweden has become the largest illegal importer of amphetamines produced in the United States, much of it shipped by pharmaceutical companies to nonexistent drugstores.

Michael Sonnenreich, of the Bureau of Narcotics and Dangerous Drugs, testified that firms do not deliberately promote illicit traffic, but "there are so many loopholes in the existing drug abuse laws. Companies crank out enormous volumes of drugs, and they sell them to anybody who appears to be legitimate." One proposal is that the federal government severely restrict the manufacture of amphetamines to what is declared to be the national need. Testimony before the Select Committee on Crime produced the scientific opinion that the "real" need of amphetamines in the United States is only "a few thousand tablets." There appears to be very little illegal manufacture of pills simply because the volume of legitimate pills is so large that they can easily be diverted to illegal distributors.

It has been estimated that 60 percent of the amphetamine pills exported to Mexico return to the United States via illegal channels. The traffic in such pills through the border town of Tijuana is so heavy that Mexican customs officials have dubbed their town "Pill City." A former drug distributor told the Committee that he made $60,000 a year by buying amphetamines in Mexico and shipping them back to the United States. He said further that he could not see "how U.S. manufacturers can send large amounts to small drugstores without knowing that illegitimate business is involved." Another pill buyer and seller told the Committee that it was a simple matter to obtain the ingredients for making amphetamines from wholesale chemical companies.

Such testimony supported demands for legislation which would limit exports and imports of amphetamines as well as the manufacture of these pills. Increased cooperation among customs officials at ports of entry also is considered essential. Recent cooperative efforts between the United States and Mexico are regarded by officials of countries as only a beginning.

It is evident that the work of police and other enforcement officers and the present level of legislation have not begun to cope with the problem of illicit drug traffic. Notwithstanding repeated raids, arrests and confiscation of drugs, traffic in illicit drugs continues to be a steadily booming business, hardly deterred by recessionary trends in the rest of the economy. Drugs continue to flow in a heavy stream into New York from all parts of the Old World and the New World. Some are shipped south to New Orleans and Houston and west to Chicago, Cleveland, Denver and Dallas. From Montreal they go to Detroit, Chicago and then westward. From Mexico City they move northward to San Antonio and then on to the West Coast, to San Francisco, Portland and Seattle. From Tiajuana they speed north to Los Angeles and on to Las Vegas. The network constantly crisscrosses the country, becoming more and more sophisticated each time.

It is apparent that a serious effort to halt the traffic in illicit drugs involves a determined attack on the problem at the very source and at the points of importation into the United States. This involves a far greater investment of both money and diplomacy than the United States has produced so far to persuade foreign governments to halt illicit production of drug materials and to secure effective enforcement of the law at points of entry into this country.

CHAPTER SIX

What Laws Can and Cannot Do

It generally is agreed that federal and state laws governing narcotics, hallucinogens, and dangerous drugs are diffuse, overlapping and contradictory. To judge by their record, they also are largely ineffective.

Drug legislation generally has been in response to citizen fear and outcry, without the prolonged study often required for effective legislation. The philosophy which seemed to prevail was "pass a law and the problem will be solved." Implicit in such laws is the assumption that they will deter practices declared to be illegal, will punish offenders and will protect society. This approach did not work with prohibition of alcohol and it has not worked with drugs. As the National Institute of Mental Health put it, "One is not dealing here with a simple, unitary phenomenon. Drug abuse is a health, legal, social, economic and moral problem. Drug abuse is a complex phenomenon in which the major interacting factors are the characteristics of the drug abused, the characteristics of the person abusing the drug, and the characteristics of the society within which the drug is abused." What is needed evidently is a long-range, carefully considered legal and educational program which is at once humane, informative and realistic.

The government, it would appear, believes this too. Its new legislation, the Uniform State Controlled Dangerous Substances

Act, tries, within its legal framework, to give courts and enforcement officers the right of individual judgment. It separates drugs into broad categories, as recommended by medical experts. It seeks to consolidate legal penalties and the obligation for drug enforcement in the office of the Attorney General. It is a step toward recognizing that there are various ways to combat drug use and all of them deserve consideration. Such was not always the case.

Initially the only legislation pertaining to drugs were pure food and drug laws. With increased opium smoking and the use of tonics of various kinds which contained opium during the early part of this century, came the first specific narcotics legislation, the Harrison Narcotic Act of 1914. This Act set up machinery for distribution of narcotic drugs, for medical purposes, within the United States. Under its provisions, all those who imported, manufactured, produced, compounded, sold, dealt in, dispensed or transferred narcotics from one location to another had to be registered and had to pay a graduated tax. In addition, it provided that all drug transactions were to be recorded on official order forms. Since passage of that Act, there have been eight other major pieces of legislation governing drugs.

The increase in the use of marihuana in the 1930s led to the Marihuana Tax Act of 1937. Under the provisions of this law it is illegal to import marihuana into the United States. This was the prime thrust of the law, since marihuana was probably first introduced into this country as an intoxicant by Mexicans and Mexican-Americans in the Southwest around 1910. The law's sponsor was the old Federal Bureau of Narcotics, which had been established in 1930. It prohibits buying, selling, transporting and concealment, and provides for permissive inference of guilt based solely on unexplained possession of marihuana.

Other specific prohibitions include the following:
- marihuana cannot be carried on a U.S. flag vessel
- an importer of the plant, called cannabis, must pay a special tax and must register with his local Internal Revenue office
- the importer must file records with the Attorney General
- marihuana transfers must be registered with the Secretary

of the Treasury

• communications facilities shall not be used to circumvent antimarihuana legislation.

The prescribed penalties under this law are, for a first offense, not less than five nor more than twenty years in jail plus a fine of not more than $20,000. For a second offense, the term span is ten to forty years and a fine of not more than $20,000. For violation of the communications portion of the Act the sentence is from two to five years and/or a fine of not more than $5,000.

To regulate opium poppy production, the Opium Poppy Act of 1942 was passed. This law made it unlawful for any citizen to cultivate the opium poppy without a license from the Federal Bureau of Narcotics. It defined opium and its derivatives— morphine and heroin—as narcotic drugs; and prohibited their importation, shipment, selling, buying and manufacture without government license. It specified further that all smoking opium found in the United States would be presumed to have been unlawfully imported and that unexplained possession of the drug was held to be sufficient evidence to authorize conviction. It likewise set up a tax stamp procedure. Opium smuggling under this law is punishable by five to twenty years as a first offense and ten to forty years as a second. An offender may also be fined a maximum of $20,000 for each offense. It further specifies that anyone making a fraudulent statement with respect to application for tax stamps or for a license to cultivate opium is liable to a fine of not more than $2,000 or a year in prison or both. The law designated the Treasury Department as the agency authorized to enforce the opium poppy provisions until 1968, when the newly formed Bureau of Narcotics and Dangerous Drugs assumed the function as part of the Justice Department.

The Narcotics Act of March 8, 1946, brought under similar controls synthetic equivalents of opium and its derivatives and such drugs as cocaine and its source, coca leaves; isonipecaine; and other "compounds, manufactures, salts, derivatives or preparations" of these drugs. It further regulates chemically produced substances which are chemically identical to any of them.

In 1956, Congress enacted the Narcotic Drug Act to establish harsher penalties for violation of drug laws, despite the Boggs Bill of 1951, which had increased the penalties prescribed by the Harrison Act. Under that first drug law of 1914, an indeterminate sentence was set for possession of unlicensed opium. A first offense for possession under the Boggs Bill brought a two- to five-year sentence, with probation permitted; a second offense carried a mandatory five- to ten-year sentence without possibility of parole. The 1956 act raised first offense penalties to two to ten years, with probation permitted; mandatory five- to twenty-year sentences without possible parole for a second offense; mandatory ten to forty years without parole for a third possession offense; and ten years to life, without probation or parole, or the death penalty if recommended by a jury, for selling heroin to an individual under eighteen. Critics of this act maintain that it takes away the American ideal of individualized justice by making degrees of punishment mandatory.

In 1960 the Manufacturing Act was passed in an effort to tighten control over legal supplies of narcotic drugs. It developed a system of licensing manufacturers and set up a quota for classes of drugs, both natural and synthetic. Special taxes are imposed on manufacturers and importers; the manufacturer is obliged to register with the Secretary of the Treasury; records must be kept and monthly statements must be rendered to the Attorney General. It specifies that only premises whose owner is licensed shall be used for drug manufacture. It makes it a violation to manufacture more than the quota of the drug specified. Conviction can result in a fine of not more than $10,000 and a prison term of not more than five years, or both. This act also allowed the Attorney General to establish basic classes of drugs, and after a hearing, to modify the list or reclassify drugs on the lists.

The Single Convention on Narcotic Drugs, 1961, came into being at a United Nations Conference held January through March 1961. It became internationally effective in December 1964 and was made a U.S. treaty obligation on June 23, 1967. Its purpose was to replace provisions of eight existing multilateral treaties and to streamline international antinarcotic control. The convention limits and regulates opium poppy cultivation and covers various drugs by name and type in separate lists. Special provisions are made, in addition to opium, for cultivation, importation and sale of coca bushes and leaves (the source of cocaine) and for the control of cannabis (the source of marihuana). It establishes the Secretary-General of the United Nations as the person who coordinates the drug listings and who passes on anything pertinent to narcotics control to the treaty participants.

Under provisions of the Convention, members agree to adhere to its strictures within their own territories, to cooperate with other nations and to limit the availability of the drugs to medical and scientific purposes. They also agree to recognize the Commission on Narcotic Drugs of the U.N. Economic and Social Council as the Convention's enforcement arm. The Commission, for its part, must amend drug lists, make recommendations to member nations and communicate these recommendations and eventual decisions to nonparties. Drugs are listed by name and quantity by member nations, as are production figures, type of use, consumption, imports and exports, stocks and seizures. Persons dealing in drugs must be listed with the Commission and must be licensed. Funding of the Commission is by the member nations, whose internal antidrug machinery is urged to work closely with the Commission.

Fifty-four nations were parties to the convention. There were exceptions. Argentina reserved the right to permit coca-leaf chewing. Burma, India and Pakistan permitted nonmedical use of opium and marihuana. Russia, Byelorussia, Czechoslovakia, Hungary, Poland and the Urkaine said they did not feel obligated to be parties to the Convention. There were other reservations by nations which did not feel that the International Court of Justice at the Hague should be the court of last resort. Nevertheless, the Convention represented the first internationally sponsored effort to control narcotics cultivation and shipments.

The Drug Abuse Control Amendments of 1965 once again tightened manufacturing controls of drugs in the United States and again increased penalties for drug sale. All registered manufacturers, processors and their suppliers, wholesale druggists, pharmacies, hospitals, clinics, public health agencies and research laboratories must keep inventories and records of receipts and sales of drugs and make them available to the Bureau of Narcotics and Dangerous Drugs. It says further that no prescription for a controlled drug older than six months can be filled, nor can refills be made more than five times in the six-month period. Under this law, illegal possession of dangerous drugs carried a maximum penalty of one year in jail, or a fine of not more than $1,000, or both. An offender may be placed on probation for a first offense. A person who illegally produces, counterfeits, sells, manufactures or possesses dangerous drugs with intent to sell may receive a maximum penalty of not more than five years in prison or a $10,000 fine, or both.

This Act is directed specifically against barbiturates, amphetamines and hallucinogens. So-called "hard" narcotics and marihuana are exempted from coverage of the 1965 Act. Because of the rising use of such drugs among the young, special penalties are provided for those over eighteen who sell or give any of the controlled drugs to persons under the age of twenty-one. A first offense carries a maximum penalty of ten years in prison, or a fine of $15,000, or both; a second offense increases the maximum prison term to fifteen years and the fine to not more than $20,000, or both.

The Narcotic Addict Rehabilitation Act of 1966 provides for the civil commitment of narcotic addicts charged with federal criminal offenses, in lieu of prosecution, and it permits a court to prescribe a treatment program instead of imprisonment. It also allows for establishment of a treatment program for addicts not charged with a criminal offense. This has been criticized as a form of preventive detention.

Although an individual court has the power either to imprison a person convicted of a crime or to recommend a treatment program, the defendant, under the Rehabilitation Act, must be found to be an addict likely to be rehabilitated. This is determined by examination by the Surgeon General's or Attorney General's office. Treatment is specified as institutional care followed by a longer on-the-street aftercare; and an addict who relapses into drug use during the aftercare period may be returned to the treatment facility for further care. The Act

Police examine 220 pounds of pure heroin, seized in one of the largest raids in New York's history. Worth perhaps $60 million after dilution, this much heroin would make close to a ton of the impure "street drug."

further states that criminal charges may be dropped following a successful treatment period. Conversely, failure to respond can result in renewal of prosecution procedures.

It can be seen from these various provisions that the laws, attempting to be specific and to plug loopholes, do overlap. This is also true in the case of enforcement authority. After passage of the 1965 Drug Abuse Control Amendments, a Bureau of Drug Abuse Control was established in the Food and Drug Administration. Thus responsibilities were given to the Attorney General, the Treasury Department, the Department of Health, Education, and Welfare and the Internal Revenue Service. In 1968, by order of the President, the Bureau of Drug Abuse Control and the Federal Bureau of Narcotics were shifted out of HEW and the Treasury Department respectively. A Bureau of Narcotics and Dangerous Drugs was created and placed under control of the Attorney General. This effort at central organization was followed by a recent attempt at consolidation of all drug laws. Several states adopted provisions recommended under a 1937 Uniform Narcotic Act. This was designed to make uniform the antidrug laws of the states, but modifications were made and continue to be made, so that state drug laws are hodge-podges.

The Uniform State Controlled Dangerous Substances Act of 1970 attempts to collate what is in previous legislation. It includes provisions defining and governing drugs such as heroin and cocaine, amphetamines and barbiturates, marihuana and other hallucinogens such as LSD. It defines manufacture, sale, production and possession. The individual states are left to determine the scope of abuse involved and the risk to public health. Courts are allowed more latitude than before in dealing with those accused of selling or possessing drugs. The law allows researchers into drugs to register with the Attorney General, thus permitting them to work with controlled drugs. Heretofore, researchers had to have state registration before they could obtain Federal registration. Since it was virtually impossible for researchers, say of marihuana, to get state registration, their work was hampered. The Act also solidifies control and enforcement under the Attorney General.

The controversial aspect of the Act is its "no-knock" provision. This would permit Bureau of Narcotics and Dangerous Drugs agents to enter premises without warning where they have reason to believe illegal drug traffic or manufacture is taking place. Opponents call it a violation of the Constitutional right to privacy. Proponents point out that before the break-in occurs a narcotics enforcement officer must apply for a regular search warrant, at which time he must present reasons why proposed seizures, searches of premises and investigation of persons would be jeopardized if announcement of intentions are made. Only after this procedure can a magistrate issue special "no-knock" authority.

The law also sets up a schedule for drugs. Generally speaking drugs in "list one" of the schedule are those which have no apparent medical usefulness but possess substantial potential for abuse. They include heroin, marihuana, peyote and various other hallucinogens, including LSD. In "list two" are drugs with a high abuse potential which also have medicinal value. These include opium, morphine and codeine. A third group also has abuse potential but is used widely for medical reasons. This includes depressants, stimulants, barbiturates and tranquilizers. Drugs in a fourth group are exempt preparations such as codeine-containing cough syrups sold over the counter in drug stores and other mild nonprescription drugs. The Attorney General can move drugs from one list to another but cannot move any drug from "list one" to any list below it without the consent of Congress. This means that the Attorney General could not, for example, legalize marihuana without legislative approval.

The Act does away with mandatory penalties and permits judges to adjudicate individuals based on past criminal records, on medical histories and on individual circumstances. It goes a long way toward making drug laws uniform—and thus more enforceable—throughout the country.

These controls represent a response to recommendations made by various conferences and study groups. A 1968 study by the California State Assembly Committee on Criminal Procedure, formed to study assumptions of drug and other criminal laws, found that there was no evidence that severe penalties effectively deterred crime; that prime deterrents were quick apprehension, certain conviction and any length of imprisonment. Likewise there was no evidence that prisoners were rehabilitated while they were incarcerated. It found that community-supervised parole led to a far greater degree of rehabilitation.

Those who favor uniform laws hope that the new Act will eliminate such legal question marks as the California law which makes it a misdemeanor, carrying a one-year penalty, to be in any room or place where marihuana is present, even if the person does not know about it; or the Colorado law where even a first-offense sale to anyone under twenty-five years of age can bring life imprisonment; or such convictions as that in Dallas where a shoeshine-stand operator received fifty years in jail for selling a box of marihuana to an undercover policeman; or the Louisiana law which specifies a five- to fifteen-year sentence even if a minor passes drugs to another minor; or a Missouri law under which a minor who passes to another minor can receive the death penalty.

The new law would establish uniform standards but would allow states to regulate. It is hoped that distinctions could be made, say, between New York, which in 1969 had 28,128 registered addicts (but probably has 100,000) and Louisville, Kentucky, which had 143 registered addicts last year.

Even those who advocate strict laws are paying greater attention to the role of education. Whereas before the tendency was to sweep the drug problem under the carpet, it is now being freely aired in public—a subject to be studied in depth. Many who have studied drugs and the laws governing them are convinced that repressive measures no longer are valid. They feel that intelligent law-making has become all the more important in view of the fact that drugs now span the whole rich-poor, black-white gamut of America, that they no longer represent simply an urban problem, that they involve not only adults but also the young.

They feel that legislation should recognize, as the National Institute of Mental Health noted: "Ours is a drug-taking society, where a host of different drugs are used for a variety of purposes—to restore health, lessen pain, induce calm, increase energy, create euphoria and induce sleep and alertness. Today many substances are available to swallow, drink, or inhale in order to alter mood or state of consciousness. Unfortunately a good number of substances which have a legitimate use are also subject to abuse." The Institute warns that there are "no simple solutions" and asks the medical community "to accelerate the kind of research which will yield the basic knowledge required for a more rational approach to the problem."

The words of Spinoza also serve as a warning against focusing solely on legislation to solve the problem:

"We always strive toward what is forbidden and desire the things we are not allowed to have. And men of leisure are never deficient in the ingenuity needed to enable them to outwit laws framed to regulate things which cannot be entirely forbidden. He who tries to determine everything by law will foment crime rather than lessen it."

PART TWO

What Young People Say

CHAPTER SEVEN

How a High School Senior Sees Drugs

In the following chapter, a high school senior
sets forth her impressions of the student "drug scene" today:
whom it involves, why they experiment, what drugs they use
and how students buy them. She also recounts the
student reaction against one school's attempt to curb
the growing trend and undertakes to explain why.

Marihuana and the more powerful psychedelic drugs, LSD and mescaline, began to circulate in my high school about three years ago, and their use has been expanding ever since. Sometimes when marihuana and the other more common drugs are scarce, bizarre substances are sampled instead.

One of my friends used to buy large quantities of cough medicine containing codeine, nose drops and nose inhalers. He would drink these in order to get high. When he was really desperate, he would buy spot remover to inhale. He and seven other students were taken to the hospital last year to have their stomachs pumped after they had been found unconscious in a room strewn with spot remover bottles. These practices, however, are not common as the most popular drugs are marihuana, the psychedelics, and more recently heroin. Those students who take "medicine chest" drugs like barbiturates and amphetamines, take them mainly as a last resort.

Three years ago, only the hippies used drugs. The majority of the students, those in sororities and fraternities, still went out drinking beer on Saturday nights. But during 1968-69, many students who were "straight" the year before began to use dope. One friend, when I asked why he started smoking marihuana answered, "Well, I was sick of hearing how good it was from some people and how bad it was from others. I wanted to see for myself."

The people who are "seeing for themselves" what these drugs can do are as varied as the drugs. They now include the children of senators and teachers, ambassadors and policemen.

My estimate is that the use of marihuana in my school has risen by 50 percent over the past three years. At present, almost everyone has smoked marihuana at one time or another. In fact, I would guess that 75 percent of the students regard "pot" as lightly as an ice cream soda, whether they use it or not.

There are a few students, however, who do not experiment. This minority consists of kids who prefer the "old ways"—the beer drinkers—and those who are scared to try any drug. A very small minority refrain because they think it is morally wrong or because they do not want to disobey their parents. Lastly, there are those who are just not interested.

Marihuana is often smoked at school. Sometimes one can catch a whiff of the sickly sweet smoke when passing the bathrooms. Students also smoke in the art rooms, in the auditorium, on their lunch break, on the front lawn and even in the halls. When someone has a birthday, a common present is a "joint" (marihuana cigarette). The fact is, I never know if my friends are laughing because they think something is funny or because they are stoned. Some people smoke marihuana daily, others only occasionally. Surprisingly, the ones who are constantly stoned are not necessarily the ones who do poorly in school. Friends of mine who claim to have "smoked" every day for two years have received good grades and have been accepted by good colleges.

Most of the real "pot" smoking is done outside of school. Although some students smoke at home, in the bathroom or the attic. most people prefer to do it in the company of their friends and away from adults, especially parents. Although a person may seem perfectly "normal" to his parents while under the influence of marihuana, he would find it difficult to disguise his state if he were caught in the house with the drug in hand.

Students have a number of ways to keep parents from discovering their marihuana. Some bury it in the yard; others just hide the pipe and drug in some inconspicuous place: in a flower pot, under the bed, in a jewelry box, in a book case, in a remote corner of the attic, or even inside a radio. The hiding place depends on the individual's house and how thoroughly his parents inspect his quarters. Most people avoid leaving any "evidence" for too long a time in such places as top drawers, purses or clothing.

Everyone says teenagers smoke "grass" to get back at their parents, but that is just not true. When a person reaches high school age, he begins doing things and discovering things for himself, regardless of what parents may think. Drug use is one of these things.

Of course, the reasons people try marihuana vary:

"I wanted to see what it was like, and I liked it."

"When people ask me why I first tried grass I try to think of some deep intricate reason for it. Actually, it just boils down to curiosity."

"My brother had been smoking the stuff for quite a while and really liked it. Finally he offered me some and I took it. I guess I always knew I would take it, but it's nice to do it with someone you love and trust the first time."

"I wanted to get high."

"I was sick of all the bad values of everyone, and I guess I associate grass with something different."

"Wow, it was so long ago I don't remember."

LSD is another popular drug among high school students. Although most students use it after school or on weekends, a few come to class "tripping" under the influence of LSD. Even a person familiar with the effects cannot always tell when someone has taken LSD. Once, I spent the whole day with a friend who told me after school that he dreaded driving home. When I asked him why, he replied that he was "tripping." I never would have known it. This is why drug use can go completely undetected by the school administrations.

LSD is used mainly by white students and, in general, it can be said that the blacks do not experiment with any of the psychedelic drugs. There are many reasons for this. Heroin and marihuana have been in the ghetto for a long time, but the suppliers of these drugs do not peddle LSD, speed or mescaline. Therefore, the psychedelic drugs are rarely available in the inner city. Also, most blacks dislike them because they are "white" drugs. One black guy, when asked why he did not take "acid," said, "What do you think I am, man, a hippie?" The only exceptions I know are those blacks who associate with or are part of the hippie culture.

LSD, which has been sampled by perhaps a third of the white students, is not used nearly as often as marihuana. One reason is that the effects last much longer, which makes it impractical to take all the time. Also, if taken too often, the drug has no effect. Finally, a general fear of the drug's effects, when used too frequently, prevents students from taking it casually. According to one girl, "I don't think I would be able to handle acid, although many people can. Besides, I would always hate myself if it caused me to have a deformed baby. I'm not saying it will, but I don't want to find out the hard way."

Other students say that the strong effects of the drug, both visual and mental, are too much to handle. One friend told me, "I've quit tripping because it is just too unreal. It scares me."

Many who have quit or limited their "trips" say they were afraid it would "mess up their heads." One observed that "tripping is nice, but it's like candy. Take it too often, and you're bound to get cavities . . . in your head."

Finally, unlike marihuana, LSD is a chemical, and for some people, this is reason enough not to take it.

Some prefer mescaline to "acid" for tripping because they do not think it is as powerful or harmful. They say this is because it is "organic." In general, organic drugs are preferred to synthetic (man-made) because their effects are believed to be more natural. One friend used a sack of poppy seeds to make an "organic drug-shake." He put the seeds in an electric blender then added milk, sugar, and a little chocolate. A few hours after drinking the mixture, he was tripping.

Heroin has been in the high school longer than the psychedelic drugs, circulating for many years among black students. Last year, several black friends told me about their experiences. They would "shoot it up" in the bathroom and then come to class "high." Often, it caused them to fall asleep there.

Towards the end of 1969, the police arrested one of these students in a bathroom in the school basement. They charged him with possession of an illegal weapon (a hypodermic needle) and heroin. Several "intruders" who apparently had been peddling heroin to black students all year were also arrested. At the time of these "busts," the majority of the white students in my school knew little about heroin. The white student was never approached by a pusher, and as a result did not know that these "strangers" were selling heroin in the halls. Of course, everyone realized that some kids, somewhere, were shooting heroin, but no one really knew the extent of the problem.

The use of heroin by white high school students is relatively new, but it is rapidly becoming popular. I think one reason for this is that students are told that heroin is a dangerous drug: that it will kill them. Many take this warning as a dare to show their "cool" and prove their bravery. Experimenting with heroin seems to have replaced the stunts that were popular among some teen-agers five years ago. One sport, called "chicken," consisted of slitting one's arm with a rather blunt razor blade. The person who quit slitting first was chicken. Still another "test of coolness" was to place a lit cigarette between the arms and then press them tightly together. The person who withstood the pain longest won. Many inflicted hole-like scars in their arms from playing this game. Moreover some teen-agers claim to know people who played Russian Roulette or practiced dangling by one arm and a leg out of speeding cars.

Several of my friends, who now are beginning to take heroin, say they use it because "man, everyone smokes grass." They seem to consider heroin "cool" because it is different. On the other hand, I know of no one who has switched from "grass" to heroin because they needed a more powerful drug to get them "high."

A high school student can purchase drugs in many different ways and for many different prices. One determinant of cost is the drug. Another is its availabality, since the price of any drug increases if there is a shortage.

The amount of money spent for marihuana by most students ranges from five to twenty dollars. A nickel bag (about ¼ ounce) costs five dollars and usually contains enough marihuana for at least five joints. A dime bag is ten-dollars' worth and an ounce normally costs between fifteen and twenty dollars. Even a nickel bag can go a long way if the quality of marihuana is good, since one marihuana cigarette can give several people a "high."

LSD and mescaline cost four or five dollars a capsule or tablet. Sometimes the drug is "two-way," which means it is doubly strong and can be shared with someone else or taken "twice" (one-half at a time).

Most students purchase marihuana, which is a relatively inexpensive drug, from their classmates or friends. There is very little secrecy among students as far as marihuana is concerned, which is one reason why it is so easy to buy. A person need only ask around, and sooner or later he will be directed to someone who is selling.

Every high school has several students who deal regularly. These students buy large quantities (pounds, kilos, half pounds) from their contacts, who are usually college students or friends of an older brother or sister. Sometimes the contact is a friend or acquaintance who graduated from high school a few years before and is now either bringing in large quantities of marihuana from abroad or else knows someone who is trafficking.

Other students grow their own. One of my neighbors raised 60 marihuana plants on his roof. When they were mature, he not only had enough for himself but also plenty to sell to his friends. He was making quite a bit of money until his father overheard a phone call concerning a sale and put a stop to the "rooftop greenhouse." Incidentally, overhearing a phone call is frequently the way parents learn about their children's involvement with drugs.

Since marihuana and LSD are relatively cheap drugs, it is fairly easy for a high school student to get money for them without arousing his parents' suspicion or concern. The most common source of income for these drugs is the student's allowance or lunch money. In addition, some students ask their parents for a few dollars to buy a book for school or to purchase a new notebook, art supplies or a lock that supposedly was stolen. Also, they may say that a class trip costs ten dollars when in reality it only costs five. This extra money actually goes toward purchasing marihuana or another psychedelic drug.

If these methods fail, some students will steal a small amount of money from a parent's purse, or drawer. Finally, students who have part-time jobs, about 5 percent of the student body, have the easiest time saving for drugs.

Purchasing heroin is usually more difficult. If a student is addicted to heroin, he can no longer rely on his friends to treat him or on his allowance to support the habit.

A high school student is introduced to heroin by a friend who offers or shows him some. This friend usually has a contact, or pusher, from whom he buys heroin. However, if the student decides to take the drug often or if he becomes addicted, he must deal with the pusher directly. The addict, moreover, may not always be able to get heroin from his particular dealer, in which case he must go out on the street and find another. This is not necessary in my high school. It is a fact known both by faculty and students that pushers actually operate in the school. These "intruders" usually pass unnoticed because they are young and look like students. Only a small percentage of the student body knows them for what they are.

Because of the presence of heroin, and subsequently of addicts, there has been an alarming amount of crime in the school. Students have had their lockers broken into and their coats stolen. In addition to personal articles such as purses, coats and clothing, much of the school's portable property has disappeared. Certain students have managed to steal most of the record players, slide projectors, copying machines, and tape recorders there. Some addicts also attempt to get money for heroin by stealing expensive dresses and jewelry from department stores to sell at school. During a lunch period last year someone offered me a grey suede dress with a $180 pricetag for only $80.

The administration has discovered very few of the culprits. Last year, only two were expelled for theft. They have also had little success in attempts to curb drug traffic in school.

Last year, narcotics agents disguised as students were planted in the school. They succeeded in arresting eight or nine kids, but they were unable to conduct any widespread investigations before their presence was discovered. After learning about these agents, a few students immediately formed a committee to warn people. Signs reading "Beware of the Bust," "Watch Out for the Mod Squad" and "Bust Coming Soon—Be Careful" were pasted all over the corridors. Every day the administration would tear down the signs, only to have new ones mysteriously appear.

Police were also assigned to the school to prevent pushers from roaming the halls and to discourage theft. For almost a month, at least five policemen constantly patrolled the halls. Most of the students protested this form of "protection." During one school assembly several·students complained that they were in a school, not the army, and that the "Mod Squad must go!"

That afternoon, almost a hundred students marched to the nearest police station, chanting "Out Police" and carrying signs. This action received a great deal of publicity. A week later, the principal requested that police be removed from the school. Now the police patrol the school grounds instead.

The most intensive, and in my opinion, the least successful method employed by the Board of Education to warn students about the dangers of drugs is the use of films and guest speakers.

In health class, students are shown films about drugs that distort and greatly exaggerate the truth. In one movie on marihuana, a boy who had just smoked a "joint" looked into a mirror and saw himself change into Wolfman. Another movie, about LSD, showed a man swallowing a capsule of acid. Two minutes later, he was tripping—rolling on the ground and screaming.

Throughout these movies, the students laugh uproariously. The lasting effect of the films, however, is contempt for the administration. Students know that no one begins to trip as soon as he swallows acid. They know that no one turns into Wolfman or into a drug addict just because he has smoked some grass. These films, and the fact that they never fail to distort the facts, only serve to make the students distrust the administration. As a result, even when the faculty brings an ex-heroin addict to school to speak about the dangers of addiction, few pay any attention because they know they have been lied to before.

The fact that some teachers "turn on" further erodes the

authority of the administrators. Although the principal obviously does not know who these teachers are, many students do. Last year, a student saw one of the younger history teachers smoking marihuana at a party. Several other teachers have occasionally joined their students for a joint after school. Others may not go this far, but neither do they conceal the fact that they do "turn on."

On the senior class trip last year, one of the teachers reportedly remarked, "I don't care what you smoke. Just don't let me see you." This statement reflects the attitude of many younger teachers, although they do not talk this way in class.

Students react to their parents' warnings in much the same way as they do to those of the school administration. After all, most parental advice about drugs is the same as the known lies students hear at school. Furthermore, it is often the P.T.A. and similar groups that insist drug films be shown. As a result, students have little regard for what parents say about drugs.

Perhaps the solution to part of the drug problem would be to educate the educators and parents first, then students might believe what they are told.

CHAPTER EIGHT

Drugs on a College Campus

A student at a large urban university
tells in the following report how the smoking of marihuana
has become a generally accepted social activity
on his campus.

For the past two years, drugs, especially marihuana, have been a key topic of conversation on my college campus. Originally, drug users were the long, kinky-haired, unshaven, bell-bottom-wearing "hippies," whom most of us, with our cuffed pants and fraternity jackets, looked upon with disdain. But it took only three semesters for us to turn down the cuffs on our pants, shed our fraternity jackets, grow our hair longer and sample drugs. We have different reasons, such as the following, to explain the switch:

- "I was an exchange student in Mexico during my junior year in high school. All the high school kids there smoke grass. I guess it seemed like the natural thing to do, so I started smoking."
- "I've always looked for new and different things to do. When I heard some guys had some marihuana to sell, I decided to try it. I liked it."
- "I was at a party one night and someone started passing out joints. When it came to me, I tried it."
- "I felt that before I could discuss the controversy over marihuana intelligently, I had to try it, so I asked some of my friends to give me some."
- "Everyone was smoking, so I decided that I might as well too."

• "It seemed that I was being left out. My friends were always getting together to smoke, but they weren't inviting me because they knew I didn't. Rather than lose contact with my friends, I decided to start smoking."

The social pressure on students to smoke is immense. Every day, more and more students begin to smoke, and the ones who hold out must be stronger and stronger. Some, of course, will always hold out. Often, they will cite the law as the only obstacle preventing them from smoking. I have one friend who is so afraid of marihuana that he refuses to come over to my apartment for fear there will be a bust. But on the whole, pressure will get to most students, and they will smoke at least once.

The first time I smoked marihuana was a Thursday night— the traditional beginning of the weekend on many college campuses. Like most of my friends, there were no Friday classes to force me to go to bed early.

When I arrived at my friends' apartment, there were already seven guys there. At one time, all had belonged to a fraternity. Within the last year, all had dropped out. The penny loafers they had once worn were scrapped in favor of sandals and moccasins. On all, moustaches, beards and long hair had replaced the "clean-cut" college look of three years earlier.

A clear plastic bag containing an ounce of finely strained marihuana lay on the floor. A package of cigarette paper and a pipe lay next to it. Strawberry incense was burning in an ash tray on the kitchen table, and "black" light flooded the room. Two joints passed from hand to hand.

After three puffs my head began to spin. After five, I felt as if I were floating. I burst into fits of uncontrollable laughter. My friends seemed to take great pride in "turning me on."

I later learned that this "grass" was the best that had hit our campus so far, and it had come at a good time. The campus had suffered a drought of marihuana for about two weeks, and this "grass" was going at $20 to $25 an ounce, as opposed to the usual $15.

Feeling that marihuana was not so bad, I decided to purchase my first ounce. One of my friends told me that he would be glad to get it for me.

He explained that this was the usual way to obtain the stuff. He would distribute about a pound for one of his friends who, in turn, would give him an ounce or two free. His friend, who would buy a kilo (about 2.2 pounds), secured enough for both profit and personal use. He would pay about $300 for a "key" (kilo), sell it for about $450 and keep a few ounces for himself. He usually bought the drug from an off-campus dealer, who might have as much as 100 pounds available. The off-campus dealer would be in it strictly for profit. He might run a small shop or bookstore as a front, but he could make as much as $5,000 a week distributing marihuana to smaller dealers. Usually, he would have a contact from the underworld who would supply him with the drug. Frequently, he would take trips out west or to Mexico to bring back marihuana.

Unfortunately, my friend was unable to get any marihuana for me. The following Monday, as I walked to one of my classes, a girl approached me and said that she had heard I was interested in buying some grass. I was surprised and hesitated. But as we walked along, I felt she could be trusted, so I told her I was interested. She said it was good stuff and, at $18 an ounce, I couldn't beat the price. We made arrangements to meet in my car parked on the quad at 10 that evening.

She approached my car that night with an armful of books and a paper bag. She waved and I motioned for her to get into the car. She sat down next to me and, while talking, took a small plastic bag containing marihuana out of the larger paper bag. Careful to keep her hands below the window level, she bent over and put it under my seat. I paid her the $18, thanked her and said goodbye.

It might have been a coincidence, but the next day while at the snack bar, a friend asked if I wanted some hash. I told him that I had just purchased some marihuana but, since I had never tried hash, I might buy some. To my surprise, right there, in full view of everyone, he reached into his pocket, pulled out a small aluminum foil-covered cube and put it in my breast pocket. He told me to try it, and if I liked it I would pay him; if not, I would return it.

Thus began a three-week streak of being stoned every night. The more I smoked, the more I felt a part of the drug community on campus. I would go from one friend's apartment to another, sometimes bringing my own stuff, sometimes not. It was always offered to me.

Though the price of drugs took a chunk out of my budget, the usual Friday or Saturday night date, with its $6 trip to the movies or $20 trek to dinner, was replaced by the stay-in evening. My date and I would get together with a few couples, smoke, listen to music and talk.

One of our chief topics of conversation would be the laws about marihuana. It was now clear to all of us that the laws could not be enforced. If the police were to arrest all the students who smoke marihuana, there wouldn't be room in the jails for all of them.

Although there is some risk involved in smoking, we feel it is so minimal that we need not be concerned about it. We do not even bother to take the precaution of locking the door and putting a wet towel under it to prevent the smell from escaping into the hallway. We even leave the door open and let the odor float out of the room.

This is pretty much the situation throughout the campus community.

The almost total acceptance of marihuana by the campus community is also seen in the increasing number of teachers who, during class, discuss and admit to the use of marihuana.

The administration is quite aware of the drug situation. Recently, I saw this official notice posted on a bulletin board in a dormitory: "A ten-pound shipment of Mescaline cut with rat poison is in the area. Do not buy any Mescaline." This notice was also published in the school newspaper and carried by the campus radio station.

Most students are content with using only marihuana or hashish. Some strongly criticize the use of hallucinogens, such as LSD and Mescaline, but not many object to the use of amphetamines, such as Dexedrine, except when used in "speeding." I use Dexedrine periodically during the school year to enable me to study all night. Nearly all students use it for this purpose. The familiar cry of, "Does anyone have a Dex?" can be heard during final exams on every floor in every dormitory.

It sells for as much as 50 cents a pill during finals when it is in greatest demand, and there are always enterprising students around with supplies of Dexedrine or other amphetamines. I have seen some of my friends go as long as three days straight without sleeping or eating after taking amphetamines.

All college students, at one time or another, come in contact with drugs. Though all will not use them, many will experiment and some will become periodic users.

Our feeling is that marihuana is here to stay—at least on the campus—and our parents and the adult world must somehow adjust to this fact.

CHAPTER NINE

A Student Smoker Speaks Out

In this chapter, a 19-year-old American college student
presents the case for drug experimentation, as he sees it,
demonstrating the gap which exists between the generations
in their approach to this issue.

Recently much time and attention has been spent studying the
alarming use of drugs by the young in our society. Numerous
books and articles have been written religiously advertising
both their beneficial and destructive aspects. Everyone from
the local priest to the newest vanguard poet has felt it his
duty to describe his latest and most "relevant" trip or high.
Our scientists, not to be outdone, have added a considerable
amount of impressive medical data, and not to be forgotten
are the somewhat comic yet tragic attempts to "educate" our
youth by our well-meaning but puritanical police. Among all
these voluminous works little is to be found explaining some
of the reasons why our youth find it necessary to turn to these
drugs. From personal experience I would hold these reasons
to be among the most important aspects of this drug problem.

Since the early fifties a new subculture has been appearing
in America. It first drew public attention under the heading of
a "Beat" culture, sporting such names as Ginzberg, Kerouac
and Bourroughs. Although the "Beat" following was minimal,
nevertheless it existed and as such it offered an interesting
and hopeful alternative way of life to a huge new generation
of youth that was born into the postwar prosperity.

This generation was born into a world filled with leisure
time and paved with wall-to-wall carpets. This world was the

dream of our parents who, having experienced the horrors of the depression and the war, had put their backs together to build a better America for us. In fact they did build a better America, but although their intentions were good, unfortunately the results turned out differently. They built us the America of their dreams; they presented us with a complete prefabricated dream house with those two long-wished-for cars and a precious television set. What to our parents was the fulfillment of a beautiful dream was, to us, just two cars, a house and a television. We lacked the deprivation through which to appreciate these gifts.

In contrast to our parents' generation, who built up their material dream, our generation has highly valued the more spiritual things of life, which unfortunately our predecessors, the "silent generation," neglected. Thus it happened that two strikingly dissimilar generations arose: one silent materially-minded generation, and one very loud, idealistic and spirtually-minded generation, the latter existing as a reaction to the former.

It was also in the beginning of the fifties that our black brothers, taking advantage of this new intellectual mood, began to climb out of their stagnant situation. It was then that we heard Malcolm X harangue his "brothers and sisters" into self recognition. He was followed by such men as James Meredith, Martin Luther King and later by Stokeley Carmichael, Julian Bond and Huey Newton, who all made the concept of black nationalism a reality.

In respect to drugs, this new feeling of black pride is important because it was from this black culture that the initial introduction to drugs came. It was among the blacks that drugs were to be found and it was from there that it spread, bringing in the marihuana, the cocaine and the heroin.

Not only did the black culture introduce drugs, but it also offered, not unlike the Beats, an alternate way of life. It gave support to the new generation of disillusioned white youths; it offered them an original life style in their search for spiritual satisfaction.

Like every new movement, the Beat generation was small and its appeal was limited. It was not until the sixties that the word spread through the news media, and this new culture gained followers: The hippies (a slang word derived from "hip" meaning a white person who associated with the black culture and who typically was found in black-frequented bars mixing with blacks). The dawn of the new hippie culture came in 1966, complete with its own news magazine cover picture and the outlawing of LSD.

Just as in the fifties the Beatniks had almost vanished from lack of press-coverage, so did this movement flourish from widespread press publicity. Like apostles, the news media spread the "good word" which sparked an excited response from a restless and disillusioned white youth. Not only was this feeling of disillusionment being felt by our restless teen-agers; slowly but with marked progress a strange un-American feeling of estrangement began to feel its way through our population. They began to feel uneasy about a distant war in Vietnam, about those strange murmurings in our ghettos, about pollution and overpopulation. The uneasiness spread, as their youths began to leave home and began actively to criticise their blinding affluence, their crippling cars, their anesthetic money, and the hyprocrisy of their seeming liberality. With each new eager run-away the list of wrongs they criticized increased until even our "American way of life" fell victim to their taunts.

Alongside us, too, a new generation of blacks had arisen and they too began to yell at the silent generation. No longer, like their Uncle Tom predecessors, were they humble enough to accept the "generous" gifts of "liberal" politicians; they felt the hypocritical degradation in these grudging gifts and in new-born fury they became a power of their own and took what was theirs. The NAACP became a hateful joke, the ghettos buzzed, black fists rose in angry defiance, and way off in the suburbs the offended liberals whispered to each other in worried paternal tones. Not only were their "adopted children" sulking in the ghetto, but also their own offspring had joined the holy war against the American way of life.

The time had come when blacks and whites, side by side, or in some sort of truce, stood up in civil war against their parents' way of life.

A conflict has begun that is assaulting the American culture on all sides. Today we see a cultural war between two incompatible ways of life and ways of thought. As each soldier fights a different war so each of us finds himself at variance with some different aspects of America, and struggles to right that wrong. The romantic fights the cold and calculating American reason, the pacifist, the draft. The Black Panthers wage a guerrilla war against racism, the SDS fight against the academic establishment, the long-hairs protest against irrational social regulations of propriety, and the drug user clamors against medieval prejudices.

In short, America now finds itself fighting not one, but two undeclared wars: One in Vietnam, another at home. To understand our "drug problem," it is necessary to see the complete field of conflict of which drugs is only one of the battles. To understand why your son or daughter "turn on" maybe you better understand that America's youth is making a bitter attempt to establish their right to run their country; they are fighting for the preservation and legalization of their culture. They no longer want to live "at home" as outlaws, and an integral part of their culture is drugs.

Little has been written or said to illuminate the immediate pressures and deterrents of "turning on." Quite simply I'd like to show what it feels like to be a young person surrounded by an impressive drug culture.

Rather than recounting my own experiences, let me explain how young people encounter drugs in (I must admit) a rather dry and factual fashion. I would like to discuss the social aspects of "turning on" from my biased experimenter's point of view.

Regardless of their parents, the police, or the medicine man's advice, young people have their own standards with which they judge drugs. Police pamphlets, parental pleas and professional advice mean little to them, whereas the examples of their own peers do impress them.

From their peers young people get a massive amount of encouragement. A liberated youth movement has adopted drugs as one of its weapons and is waving it in defiance across

America. Bob Dylan's song "Everybody Must Get Stoned!" has an unmistakable message. The Beatles tell us to "Do it in the Road" and Grace Slick sings that we should "Feed our Heads!" Tom Wolfe's book, *The Electric Kool-Aid Acid Test,* tells of how Ken Kesey traveled across America spreading the word about LSD. Timothy Leary's book, *High Priest,* is a collection of trips, and Jack Kerouac has published accounts of his "stoned" adventures from Oregon to Mexico. The movie, *Easy Rider,* tells of two freaks who made their money selling cocaine, then traveled to New Orleans smoking and tripping along the way. Our psychedelic posters try to recreate trips, and our "head shops" sell hash pipes and other paraphernalia. What more encouragement do we need?

Our whole youthful culture highly emphasizes drugs and their liberating lessons. Our heroes are drug handlers, our songs praise drugs, and our poetry is drug-inspired. Our culture advertises the use of drugs everywhere, encouraging us to try them and get stoned!

Not only are we receiving cultural encouragement, but we are also being pressed by our friends' enthusiasm. Within our own immediate ranks lies the greatest advertisement for "smoking," namely the reputations and performances of our friends who smoke marihuana. One need only observe the long-term effects of drugs on close friends to see if they are, in fact, good or bad. Encouragement from friends is probably the greatest advertisement, for what friend would encourage another to try something bad—certainly no friend of mine!

With this massive encouragement it is quite understandable why we are quite undaunted by authoritarian attempts to repress this outlaw practice.

For young people in an urban society it is almost impossible not to encounter drugs, and most who do encounter them will eventually for one reason or another try them. Those who do not must have strong arguments against drugs, or a strong will to preserve their original intentions; but most people do not have the arguments or the will, and so they finally try it.

On the contrary, most people are curious to take it, and will jump at the chance to get "turned on." After a short while of holding in marihuana smoke they have "turned on" and are "stoned." Scratch another notch into your pipe!

Honestly said, getting "stoned" is most enjoyable and most smokers will agree with me. That's why most people who have turned on once won't stop there. No, they're not "hooked," they just enjoy it, and won't be averse to getting "turned on" again.

Usually it takes a while for a person to learn how to smoke properly, and so at first he won't get high. But after a few times he will suddenly forget he is holding the pipe, and looking down he will realize how stoned he really is. Getting stoned occurs in his mind and it takes a while for the inexperienced smoker to recognize that he really is stoned.

After getting acquainted with smoking and actively participating in it, smoking will usually begin to mean something else to the smoker than just a giddy head and a hungry stomach. Many people don't smoke marihuana just to get stoned; for them, smoking is a vehicle in their search for something, and, depending on what they are looking for, smoking will take on other meanings, and will become important to them in other ways.

For some people smoking is a vehicle toward social acceptance; for others, it is a sign of protest against parental authority, against the Establishment, or both. For others it means many different things. Some are looking for self-awareness in its euphoria, others seek a peace of mind. To some it is also a quick convenient badge which they can cite for their record to affirm their membership in the "Revolution." The individual can use "smoking" to mean anything he wants; it becomes his "outward sign of an inward grace." Like a mirror he can see in it what he wants and, if he needs to, he can proudly wear it as his emblem of belonging to something.

Unlike the "straight" society, there exists among smokers a feeling of brotherhood, a feeling of participation in an underground activity. This feeling is most evident in new converts who usually want desperately to belong. Unfortunately, although it sounds like a great idea, it has a negative side which can cause many to drop previous friendships in preference for fellow smokers, and through this, to lose more and more the ability to communicate with "straight people." This is why one often finds a deep gap of misunderstanding, mistrust, and self-ishness between "straight" groups and their "freaky" counter-parts.

Another negative aspect of smoking is that many new converts, through their voluntary isolation from the straight world, lose all sense of other values, and begin, in their drug enthusiasm, to judge everybody and everything in terms of their own drugged selves. Everybody who doesn't smoke is a fink, classical music is rot, and parents are necessarily always wrong. The more drugs one takes, the better; and the longer one's hair is, the better the person. These are natural reactions of overenthusiasm and are known as "getting hung up on drugs." Fortunately, these symptoms usually disappear with continued use, but in the process people often get hurt in one way or another. Many young people get so hung up on drugs that when they can't get anything to smoke they will turn to spot remover, cough syrup, and other various harmful drugs, and many get hurt this way.

After smoking for a while, most people "mellow," and their enthusiasm fades. They see things in a clearer light which some call "growing up." Their smoking at this point may decrease and become calmer. Their imagined need disappears and they can go for long times without wanting to smoke. Curiously enough, we now begin to see among our own ranks a case of generation gap, for the young enthusiast is far removed from the bearded veteran.

Finally, there are deeper problems that smoking "dope" brings about. Though most of the previously mentioned "hang-ups" diminish in time, there are two which grow with time. These two aspects seem to be deeper and further-reaching problems which could affect the user in harsher and longer-lasting ways.

The first problem, or question, is whether smoking marihuana may lead to harder drugs. Unfortunately I feel smoking pot will lead to strong drugs. Many young people who have experimented with marihuana have learned from experience that, in fact, it is not as dangerous as advertised by the media, the police and other "experts." Having seen from experience the hypocrisy that these authorities exercise, they tend to disregard any further advice about other drugs.

Many young people will progress from marihuana to other psychedelic drugs, such as LSD, Mescaline, Psilocybin (A Mexican mushroom), peyote. The use of heroin, opium, cocaine, speed, barbiturates and sundry other drugs is not as popular as the use of psychedelic drugs, but nevertheless it does exist in considerable quantity.

Though many will experiment with these stronger drugs, such as LSD, most young people will not become regular users, mainly because LSD and these stronger drugs demand a greater mental effort. Most of the young aren't looking for a religious experience; they only want to relax and get a little stoned, listen to music, and enjoy themselves for a while. LSD, in contrast to marihuana, is a far deeper and more exhausting experience, as are the other true psychedelics.

As for heroin, cocaine and opium, most young people will find it much harder to come across these drugs because their use is not widespread. Further, most young users are definitely afraid of becoming addicted, and this will deter them. Some go on to "speed," but even the young people look down on this, as they do on the use of such addictive drugs as heroin. "Speed kills" is the expression and many young people have seen it kill, and know; the others won't find much encouragement to "shoot speed."

In short, smoking may lead to further drugs, but in most cases this will happen only in terms of infrequent experimentation with LSD, for instance, or trying opium once. The great majority of young people may smoke, but won't go to stronger drugs on a regular basis.

The other problem is the law and its effects on the smoker. I feel the greatest problem facing the regular smoker stems from the illegality of marihuana. Because marihuana furthers a greater self-awareness, it may also, under certain conditions, create in the user a sense of paranoia. Though this paranoia probably stems from a frightened reaction to greater self-awareness, this fear can be transferred, and can become associated with police, and the "authorities." Depending on the situation, this paranoia can greatly increase to a very uncomfortable stage. In many cases this symptom will disappear when the users can finally accept that they *are* "outlaws," and are living "underground," but for some people the acceptance of this fact is hard.

There are many people who want to feel that what they are doing (in this case, smoking marihuana) is not an irresponsible act but a wholesome relaxation. They want to feel that they are being responsible, either to themselves or to society, but as long as the law opposes this activity they will only find frustration and handcuffs at the end of their attempt to demonstrate their own sense of values. For these basically honest people the law which should protect them instead destroys their security, for they are continually battling the law within themselves. Unfortunately, the only remedy for this problem is either to stop smoking or to lose that sense of conscience which forces the issue.

In conclusion, I have tried to explain how many young people who regularly use marihuana feel. I have tried to explain their problems and the pitfalls which confront them. It was my purpose to demonstrate that there are responsible and well-meaning people who smoke marihuana, and that unfortunately for them they will always feel the pressures of our society's persecution. It is sad when the honest must suffer through the ignorance of the complacent.

As a last thought I would ask you to compare the religious persecution of our ancestors in Europe to this cultural persecution that we face today. I would remind you that these ancestors even left their native lands to escape this persecution and come to America. Isn't it possible that we, too, may leave our homeland to escape our persecution. In fact, this emigration has already begun, as more young people every month are settling in Canada, in Europe and even in Africa.

CHAPTER TEN

A Young Woman Tells Her Story

Following is the verbatim account of a conversation
with a young woman who escaped from drug addiction
and undertook the rehabilitation program of Daytop Village,
New York City. She relates her experiences to readers
of this book in the hope that they may contribute
to an understanding of the drug problem.

Would it be of any use to tell kids of your story?

Yes, I think it would because of what happened to me when I
tried using drugs to escape from reality. Also, because the
things that happened to me are similar to things that happen to
many kids. When I started off, I was just very curious. I
wanted to be with the "in crowd," more or less, and the same
thing goes on today. Everyone wants to feel a part. So they
go into it, first for curiosity and kicks but then after a while
they depend on it. Because of this dependency, it can lead to
the actual hard narcotics, such as heroin, cocaine. The way I
started myself was on marihuana.

You started with marihuana?

Yes, I did, when I was in high school and the thing was that
I was really just using it occasionally at first. Because I enjoyed the kick that it gave me, the feeling of being high, I
started depending on it and I would use it all the time.

We are told that marihuana is not habit forming.

No, it's not habit forming, but after a while if you keep using it, you think you feel a lot better about yourself at the time you are using it because it gives you sort of a lift or a high. But the reality is, as soon as you come down from that, the reality is right in front—you are again faced with reality so you have to start all over again. It becomes a hassle more or less.

You feel then that you do become dependent on marihuana?

For me, I did, because I couldn't be happy unless I was feeling good, feeling high. That's why I smoked it more and more, and then finally that wasn't even enough for me.

You say you smoked it more and more. How many did you start with?

Occasionally, like at a party or after school, social thing, or when all the guys and girls were getting together at somebody's house, just fooling around, you know, more or less hanging out, and I would do it and then after a while it became a dependency for me, I feel because I couldn't be happy unless I was feeling high, and then it led on to barbiturates and amphetamines because the high that I got from the marihuana was not enough. It didn't satisfy me, and I still would smoke it but I would be taking barbiturates and amphetamines also. When I got into the pill scene, it was very hard for me to get away from it, because I did get a habit on barbiturates and amphetamines and it was quite hard for me to kick it. The thing was that I only felt more depressed as time went on.

After the barbiturates and amphetamines, what happened then?

I continued with those for a while, plus I was smoking marihuana also, and then I got into the scene where the people I started hanging out with, you know another crowd, were snorting heroin and cocaine, and I tried this thinking, wow, I can even feel better on this as it would be stronger. Then I started skin popping as you call it, injecting it into the skin, and finally I started mainlining. That's when I caught the habit.

That's when you really got hooked?

Yes.

Before you did that, did you already have any feeling as to the risk you were taking?

I had an idea. But at the time I was taking drugs, I really didn't look at it. I really didn't care, in other words. I really didn't care what happened as long as I could feel good.

You already were a dropout, in effect, and so you were quite ready to take almost anything that would give you a kick, take you out of this world. Is that about the way you felt?

Yes.

Could you tell us how it happened? Who were the kids that you were with? Were these kids that you knew at school?

Yes, in school. Some were from well-to-do families and some were from families that had to work hard for a living. It was more or less mixed.

Where was this? What city are we in?

I had fooled around when I was in Texas, when I was in Vermont, and in New Jersey, and then I would come into New York at different periods of time to cop and get the drugs that I needed. I went to a Catholic grammar school. This was in New Jersey, in Hackensack, New Jersey, which was the next town from me because it was a new school that had just opened and my father sent us over there. After completing Catholic school I went into junior high, a public school. I graduated from junior high, 8th and 9th grade, and went on to high school in Teaneck, my hometown. I graduated from high school and I worked for a year as a nurses' aid in the hospital in my town, in Teaneck. And then I decided that I wanted to go into the nursing field. I put in an application for nursing school and I was accepted. I graduated. I specialized in psychiatry, that was the field that I was most interested in because it was more on a people level, and in a lot of ways I did get satisfaction out of it, and I learned a lot of things about life in general. But I did get a very good feeling while I was working as a nurse, which I did for about three years until I finally collapsed because of the use of drugs and whatever.

Going back though to when you were starting with drugs. Was this in your high school period, or before high school?

Well, during the summer before my second year in high school, I was about 15.

Do you remember the first time—how it happened?

I was with my friend. She had some marihuana and asked me if I would like to try it and I said, "Yes," just being curious.

Was it a little bit like smoking any first cigarette?

Yes, feeling big and important, and then I smoked the marihuana cigarette and at first I didn't think it was anything. What I was feeling wasn't what I thought I was going to feel.

What did you think it was going to be?

I thought it was going to be like all of a sudden when you're really drunk and you don't know what you're doing. It wasn't like that at all.

What was it like?

It was just a feeling of being light-headed but knowing what I was doing, what actions, etc., and what I was talking about still.

But obviously it was a pleasant feeling to have had, and that encouraged you to go on doing it again and have some more?

Yes.

Then, as you continued, marihuana became a daily thing?

Yes, it did.

And then what happened? Did it get dull? Did it loose its excitement?

Yes, it wasn't enough for me after a while, because all through this period I was using it I was still copping out on myself, not facing different responsibilities that I had.

What do you think was driving you to cop out?

Well for one big thing I was lonely. Even though I had a lot of friends I always felt apart in some way.

Was that a fault of yours, or a fault of your parents?

No, it was a fault of my own. This was a feeling that I had inside, and rather than talk to someone about it I would hold onto it and it would just get bigger and bigger.

What was the reason for that? A sense of inferiority?

Yes, lack of confidence.

Would parents have had something to do with that?

No. When I was younger, I think when I was about 12 years old, was the first time I got in trouble, which was in school, and my parents had to go up on numerous occasions because of my behavior.

What sort of trouble?

With the teachers in the class room.

Usual kids' stuff?

Yes. One time it was after school and I was on the playground and we were fooling around throwing rocks into the windows. I don't know what you'd call it at that age, vandalism, or what. The police came to the house and I was picked up and I had to go to sign some papers at the police station, and my parents were called. On another occasion, I did the same sort of thing just down the street from me with the bunch of kids that I was hanging out with; it was concerning this woman's house; we were throwing rocks and lighting fires and everything. The police were called once again and I was pulled in and I had to go to court. And from there it really started. From there I completely resisted any type of authority.

This was from age 12?

From about 12. I resisted any type of authority, I didn't want to listen to anything anybody was telling me. I just wanted to do things my own way.

Why?

I don't know. I think more or less I had a lot of resentment. Just because of the way I was feeling. I had always felt in some way rejected.

Is this from the home again?

Well, yes, but it's nothing that my parents had to do with. In a lot of ways my parents did show me responsible concern but I would always pull away from it. I didn't want to hear anything. There is so much that your family can tell you or try to do for you, and then it's up to you.

In other words, you don't have the feeling your own personal problem began at home? No problems with a sister or a brother?

123

Well, I was very jealous of my younger sister.

Was she very close in age to you?

No, she is a few years younger than me, not too much younger.

Did your parents favor the younger sister perhaps? Did you feel abandoned by them?

I felt that they did, but now looking back at it, yes, I felt that she was favored. I felt that they loved her more than me.

Could this have started you into a rebellious frame of mind at that time? If you were going to look for any one reason, could it have been that?

Yes, because I was very jealous of her in many ways. She was a lot brighter than myself as far as school work.

If you were 12, how old was she then?

She was about 9 or 10.

Did your father love her more?

Yes, I felt that my parents *did* love her more.

Both mother and father?

Yes, at that time, because with me it was a big problem. I have a twin sister also, and my twin sister and I have always been very close. But the thing was that when I was younger I was told that I was adopted, my twin sister and I were adopted, and the thing was that my mother was told that she couldn't have any kids. And then two years later she got pregnant and had my younger sister, and when she came into the picture at first I doted over her and everything. I loved her, but as she was growing older I became very very jealous of her, feeling that my mother loved her a lot more than me, and I think this is what started me. But the thing was, now that I look at it, she was not in any way favored, but at that time I thought so, growing up. I felt rejected. I didn't feel as loved as she was. I felt that I was being cheated of something that she was getting.

Did this lead to conflict between you and your mother and father? Did it ever come to a point where they beat you?

They hit me. They didn't actually beat me.

What about your twin sister, did she have a similar feeling that you had?

I think for a time she did, but my twin sister and I are very much different in the respect that she was much quieter than I was when I was younger. When I was younger I was very wild, very out-going with any person. I would jump right into the picture, where my twin sister was very quiet and shy, and it would take her a while to adjust to any given situation. In that way we were different. As we were growing up, we did talk about our younger sister getting this, and we not. This type of thing, the cattiness that goes on in families.

What's happening to your twin sister? Did she have a drug problem?

No, she has never touched drugs.

And you never involved her in any way?

No, she has never been involved but I did talk to her about it. She did know about two years ago; up until then nobody in my family knew, but I did tell my sister first.

As you were growing up did you ever ask her to come along and smoke with you?

I think I asked her if she wanted to try it once. She said,

"No," but I had never bothered her after that. She was not in the crowd that I hung out with.

I think we have some idea of what started this thing off. It seems to start in the family.

I think the biggest thing with me was the lack of communication between my parents and myself. This, I feel, is the most important thing now.

If you were to relive your life and go back to age 12, what would you do to avoid what has happened?

I feel the thing I would do, which I never did, I would look at my parents as friends, as authority figures but also as friends, somebody I could go to at any time just to sit down and rap and talk to.

How could that have been achieved? Was it something you would have done, or your parents?

Well, both. It would have to have been a fifty-fifty thing. And for me, when I was growing up, I felt that it was only a one-sided thing. They had tried everything they could, you know, psychiatrists, everything, and I resisted every single thing they had tried for me.

You had psychiatric treatment?

Yes, a couple of times, from when I was about 15 or 16. When I was in high school and from there on up, and then two years ago I had a nervous breakdown and I was locked up for a time, and then at other different times I was locked up for different kinds of treatment. I tried to commit suicide a few times, and there was nothing left for them to do but put me somewhere I would be protected from myself.

What's your feeling about the psychiatric treatment?

My own personal feeling about that is, going through what I went through was more or less kind of a horror for me. But as far as the psychiatrists themselves, I felt it was only a job for them, a 9 to 5 thing. I felt that after working hours they forgot me; they weren't really thinking about me.

Did psychiatry help in your case?

In my case, no.

Do you have any idea as to why it didn't help?

Yes, I do now. Being in Daytop I learned why. The lack of identification. Before coming to Daytop, I know not only for myself but for other people at Daytop who have been to psychiatrists and different places for therapy and treatment— there was always that lack of identification. In other words, it wasn't one ex-drug addict to another, as it is now for me, where other people can *feel* what I am feeling and what I am going through, and we can work it out together by sitting down and talking and being honest with each other and trusting each other. Whereas all the psychiatric work that was given to me did not do that for me because I had no trust. Therefore I wouldn't relate honestly about myself and what was really bothering me. A lot of it was very superficial, going right over the surface and not hitting on the point that really needed to be stressed. The lack of trust, the lack of concern. How could they understand how I am feeling if they have never been a drug addict?

In other words, you feel you have got to have someone who is very much concerned before you can sort of open up? Is that the idea?

Yes, because I feel that without the identification there really couldn't be that much meaning.

Is the theory then that if you do open up this can be sort of brought out to the surface and then you can improve yourself?

127

You have to look at it because it is a reality, which is something I never looked at before, and now I am looking at it and I am accepting it, and I am doing something about it.

You used the word "horror" in speaking of what you've gone through. How would you describe the horror?

The reason I call it a horror is because, looking back at it now, it *was* a horror for me because I was very very scared and I felt that I was all alone in the world, and there was no one that could help me, and I kept running and running. It was like a continuous thing. It was like a big hassle, and I think the biggest horror for me was the feeling that I was holding on to inside, that was like eating away at my belly and would cause me to completely turn away from society. And for me, I became a loner and I wrapped myself up in a very hard shell and I wouldn't let anyone in. It was like being imprisoned in myself. I think it's something emotional and I felt inside that I couldn't escape from it, except through drugs, and this is why I kept running and kept using drugs; it was like a cycle, it kept going and going.

What was frightening you?

What was frightening me? Well, I was frightened by many things. I was frightened by responsibilities, by people in general, how people were looking at me. Afraid that I wasn't going to be accepted by anyone. Getting more depressed and depressed as time went on, which is why I had a complete nervous breakdown. I tried to kill myself because I felt that I couldn't run any more. I was tired of running and I felt like it was useless.

Who are you running from?

I am running from myself.

What does that really mean?

I think by running from yourself, you don't want to face yourself and the things that could make you a better person, the changes you would have to go through in order to become somebody important, somebody that you could feel respect for, which I never felt. I think the reason why I kept running constantly was because I was looking for something and I really never found it until I came to Daytop.

What were you looking for? What were you running from and running to?

I kept running because I never felt satisfied. I think what I was running from was everything that I had mentioned before. Running from the feeling of being rejected, running from the feeling of being lonely.

Didn't you have any boy friends?

Yes, I did but I never felt that I was somebody special. I felt used by a lot of guys. I didn't feel they really cared about me for *me*, but something they may have been able to get out of me.

There was no feeling of love involved in any relationship?

There was a feeling of caring to a point, but the feeling of love—no. I never felt loved, never. And I think this is really the thing I was running from and looking for. Because I did get love from my people, you know, from my family, in many ways, but I never felt it even though it was showed to me. I never felt it inside and I think the running was more or less trying to find something and someone.

You were looking for love?

Right. Looking for someone special and I never really found him.

Have you found this now?

Yes. Since I came to Daytop I realize the one important thing, that people can love each other for themselves, not for anything they might want to get out of the person, you know, anything material.

Then you have the feeling of affection in love without necessarily any physical contact? Sex does not have to be a part of it?

No, not at all, because in Daytop, unless you have a relationship, you really don't have one special person. There are a lot of special people that you feel loved by and that you love in return for just being them. Being honest and just trusting each other is a big part of that love.

Do you feel that if you had not come into some feeling of affection in love you would have not been able to solve your problem?

No, I think I would still be running.

Is this true of the other kids too? Is it the same kind of situation?

For the large majority, yes.

In other words, the factor of love was central to the whole picture.

Yes, I feel that. People describe love in so many ways, and I don't think there is one specific definition for love. Love is many things and a lot of people don't realize that. A lot of people think love is just sex. A lot of people think love is the material things that you can give someone, and then they will feel the real love. It's a majority of things. I don't think it's one specific thing.

As a kid, say, going back to 15, 16 or 17, did you think you were going to find love through sexual relations?

Yes, I did.

Did you, at that time, think that the two words were synonymous?

Yes, I did.

And then you discovered that was not so?

Yes, I did.

How does one find that this is not so?

By being rejected after having a sexual experience.

Then the drugs come as an alternative to escape from the disappointment of being unloved, for the disappointment in sex and in everything else?

Right. Drugs are only the escape; drugs were not the problem. Drugs were the way to go. Drugs were the symptom of the problem, not the cause, and I feel that this is the way with everyone.

And it certainly wasn't the cure?

Right.

Regarding the drug experience itself, how would you describe that?

Well, while it was nice to escape, the feeling of being frightened and scared was wondering if I would really return to myself. Being out of this world was nice for a period of time but I didn't want it for always.

Why not?

I really didn't want to die.

It wasn't necessarily dying. It's living out of this world, isn't it?

Yes, but the feeling of not being able to return.

Why would you want to return if there was nothing to return to?

I don't know, I guess it was just the feeling of just being scared of death.

If you enjoyed yourself in a drug world, why not go on living there?

Because I was still alone, in my drug world.

In other words, the drugs did not provide the answer either? You still felt the need for something else?

Right. Even though I was high and feeling light-headed and feeling good superficially, underneath it all I was still feeling the same way, and I was still feeling very lonely, and this alone caused me to be very frightened and scared, even while I was using the drugs and knowing that the drugs would only last for a period of time; I would be right back where I started anyway.

After they wore off, you mean.

Right.

How did you feel after they wore off?

Very depressed, very lonely and very scared. The same as I felt before using the drugs and it got worse and worse after each time I used it, by using more and more drugs, using it in larger uqantities.

How did you develop the will to want to do something to come out of it?

When I was released from the state hospital I returned home to my family, and I was out on the street for three months, and I was more or less starting the same vicious cycle once again, and I did try to kill myself once again. And I was locked up again for a period of two months. During this period of time it was told to me that I could not return to the street because I would harm myself again, and it was something that had to be done. While I was locked up, one of the personnel that worked in the psychiatric ward gave me an article on Daytop Village. I had no idea what Daytop Village was all about. At the time it really did not interest me that much, but I felt that I had to go there in order to get away from where I was. I was taken to the Swan Lake facility in New York State, and I was interviewed and I was accepted. I was still more or less in my shell, depressed, feeling very lonely and not knowing anyone there. I felt this way for a period of time.

Since I have been in Daytop, which is almost a year now, a lot of things have been pointed out to me about myself; things that now I can accept; things that I am changing. When I came into Daytop, I had no motivation to help myself. I was expecting a psychiatrist or a doctor, someone to do it for me. The biggest thing is, it is a self-help program, and it is up to the person himself. The motivation that the person has when he comes to Daytop is that it's another place that I can go, to lay up and get what I can out of it, and then return once again to society, go through the same hassles that I went through.

When I was in Daytop for 6 or 7 months I was growing up. I was becoming more of a woman, learning to accept responsibilities, which became larger and larger as my time in Daytop lengthened. Now my motivation is much greater than it was when I came into Daytop. Now I know I can do something for myself and I don't have to feel like a loser any more. I feel like I am winning a battle that I thought I would never win in my life.

Do you feel that if you were to go out of here right now that you have enough build up, enough in the bank so to speak, that you can keep on going?

No, because I feel that if I did not complete the program I know I would be missing out on other things that I still have to work through, such as socializing, getting the exposure for our "reentry" process—working in our office, helping addicts out on the street and pulling them into Daytop. This is going to be a big exposure for me. Then there is the last process of the Daytop program before graduation, when I will be exposed to the community throughout the day, getting a job, being responsible, fulfilling a lot of things, getting involved with people in the job, and going through different processes that people go through every day.

How much time is involved in the program?

The program is 18 to 24 months, and I feel that if I did leave before that period is up I would be copping out once again.

Is that because you don't have the will?

No, not because I don't have the will but because at this point I am still not a well-rounded individual. When I graduate, I will be. The directorship will evaluate me to see whether I am a well-rounded individual, have completed the Daytop program and feel that I am a whole person.

If you are a well-rounded individual, what would you be like?

I will be a woman; I will be a respected woman; I will respect myself.

What would you be then that you are not right now?

I think I would be an individual that would be able to face up to different feelings of rejection from people in society, different feelings of hurt, and more or less a whole sense of not having to fall back and trying to run, because there are still areas I still have to work through.

Do you have feelings that you sometimes want to run away and go back to the drug?

No, now I don't think about getting high any more. Well, I do occasionally, but not as much as before. Before, if I go through the littlest change or rejection or hurt or whatever it would be, I would want to get high, I would want to run and say "the hell with it." Now I realize I can't do that any more because I would be doing the same thing that I was doing before I came into Daytop, saying "the hell with it" and running. I am tired of running.

You feel that you would be killing yourself in a way?

Right, and I would be defeating my own purpose. I have been in Daytop now a year and I have worked through so many different things about myself, and it has helped me to become a much better individual; I feel a lot better about myself as a person.

One last thing. How can we reach kids on the subject of drugs? We are told that they regard Art Linkletter as a "square" (perhaps because he's an adult), and they are not interested in hearing of his daughter's tragedy. How can we approach them so that they might listen to stories such as yours?

You can say so much and put it down on paper. Then it's up to the individual. If he wants to read it and if he wants to do something about it, then he can learn from a person who has used drugs, and he can see the price we must pay for using drugs.

PART THREE

What the Experts Say

CHAPTER ELEVEN

A Judge's View of Marihuana

Testimony of G. Joseph Tauro,*
Chief Justice, Massachusetts Superior Court, before the
House Select Committee on Crime, September 26, 1969

 I do appreciate your invitation to speak to you briefly. I have prepared a statement that I wish to make. In presenting the statement, I am mindful that I rarely, if ever, am sorry for what I do not say, but very often, things that I do say come back to haunt me, and in an area of great controversy such as this, where emotions are involved, and a great deal of quotes and misquotes, I think it is best, in view of the position that I hold, to make my presentation in the form of a written memo.

That does not, I assure you, preclude you gentlemen from asking me any questions following this so long as it remains within the confines of my responsibility as chief justice and as a judge.

I think every witness who appears before a group, whether

*Judge Tauro, considered to be one of the outstanding authorities on narcotics and dangerous drugs, has served as chief justice of the Massachusetts Superior Court since 1962. He is a member of the Advisory Council of Judges of the National Council on Crime and Delinquency. In 1967, he presided at a landmark trial during which the legal status of marihuana was disputed. His decision, later upheld by the Supreme Court of Massachusetts, reaffirmed the constitutionality of the Narcotic Drug Act which outlawed the drug.

it be a court or a committee or a commission, should state his qualifications on the subject matter, especially for the record. It may well be that some of you, as you have indicated, have some idea of my background. But the cold record someday, reviewed by somebody else, may raise a question as to how come a judge dares to go into the field of science and differ with doctors and people in that discipline. For that reason, I think briefly, for the record only, I should state my qualifications.

Whatever knowledge and insights I have in the area of drug abuse come largely from 5 years of continuous service between 1963 and 1968 in the first criminal session of Suffolk County, which is the busiest criminal court of the Commonwealth, where I disposed of hundreds of serious criminal cases, including more than 250 cases of specific violations of narcotic and harmful drug laws. Many of the other cases disclosed a history of drug involvement as well. This period has coincided with the development of drug abuse as a major social problem throughout the country. Although I promised myself that I would stick closely with the script, I have to digress for just a moment by saying an example of what I was talking about was presented to you yesterday. I read in this morning's paper, I believe, that a witness appeared before you and disclosed his experience with marihuana and other drugs. Well, this happened to me—I was going to say dozens—hundreds of times, throughout the 5 years that I sat almost everyday in a busy criminal court.

My education concerning marihuana was greatly enhanced in 1967 when I presided at a 2-week trial in the so-called marihuana case. The specific issue involved then was the constitutionality of our Narcotic Drug Act as applied to marihuana. But central to the dispute was a factual determination of the nature and effects of marihuana which, on the basis of the evidence produced at the hearing, I found to be a dangerous and harmful drug.

I came to this conclusion after hearing the examination and cross-examination of 18 expert witnesses from this country, Great Britain, Greece and India. These learned and articulate men represented the fields of medicine, botany, pharmacology, psychiatry, sociology, psychology, philosophy, religion and law enforcement.

I wish to emphasize the cross-examination phase of this hearing. It is one thing for an expert to speak or write without fear of confrontation or contradiction. It is quite another when such utterances are subjected to the scrutiny of a judicial process where every statement and opinion offered for acceptance is subjected to searching cross-examination by opposing counsel.

I can assure you gentlemen that, in that case, there were two outstanding counsels who participated. In such a procedure, in my opinion, truth and logic are more apt to surface over positions which cannot be supported or substantiated.

After weeks of careful consideration of the evidence and the law, I concluded that the pertinent statute suffers from no constitutional impairment and, further, that marihuana is a harmful and dangerous drug. Upon appeal, my decision was sustained by the supreme judicial court of Massachusetts.

As an interesting footnote, later an identical issue was raised in Florida involving a similar offense and the same constitutional questions. Counsel in that case, by stipulation, presented at the trial the entire record in my case for the Florida trial judge's consideration, including a transcript of the testimony and my opinion. I state with due modesty, I hope, that my findings and rulings of law were adopted in toto by the Florida superior court judge, and on appeal his decision was sustained in the highest court of that State.

It is the only case in the country, so far as I know, that has received this type of adversary hearing—that is, involving the question of marihuana, the statutes and the harm and danger feature.

That in essence is the reason why I have had, I was going to say, the courage and audacity to come in and speak on a subject which is usually reserved to those having the disciplines. I feel that, having seen hundreds of cases, heard examined doctors, psychiatrists, examined the probation records of many people involved with drugs and marihuana, heard their association with crime, heard them testify, I believe these were conclusions that I could substantiate and justify.

I am mindful, of course, that marihuana use creates problems for adults as well as adolescents, but I believe that the danger to the user is far more serious in its application to teen-agers.

Furthermore, the older person has, hopefully, maturity of judgment, if he cares to exercise it, and therefore responsibility for the consequences to himself and to others is his and his alone.

You notice, I differentiate there the harm to the person who uses and the harm that is caused to society. The youngster's welfare, on the other hand, is our moral responsibility, and the guidance and help he requires we are duty bound to provide.

I will therefore direct my remarks first to the adolescent user and the grave problems he creates for himself and for society and second to the harm and danger to which the public may be exposed by the adult users of marihuana.

In March of this year, I was privileged to address the Massachusetts Drug Dependency Conference. There I said that the public, especially our youngsters, is subjected to conflicting and confusing theories about marihuana. Today this confusion persists. Because of the time limitation, I will confine my remarks today largely to exploring the reasons for this confusion and also its harmful effect on the very people we are trying to help.

Basically, one of the most important and underlying reasons for this confusion is the failure to place sufficient emphasis on those harmful qualities of marihuana on which there is no substantial disagreement among reputable and informed authorities. Now, you may well say, well, now, by what authority do you have to say in the areas that I am trying to delineate, on the realm of no dispute: from the very fine experts who testified before me. I went through that stack of transcripts with a fine-tooth comb and there is no substantial difference of opinion, whether they testified for the Commonwealth or testified for the defendant on these points where I say there is no disagreement.

First, marihuana is universally recognized as a mind-altering drug which, in varying degrees and with unpredictable effect, produces a state of intoxication sometimes referred to as "euphoria."

Second, in varying degrees this state of intoxication or euphoria may cause a lessening of psychomotor coordination and a distortion of the ability to perceive time, distance and space. However, there is usually no resulting diminution of muscular strength. I emphasize that last point because I will refer later as to its importance. It affects his thinking and everything else, but the strength is usually not affected.

Third, the habitual use of marihuana is particularly prevalent among individuals with marginal personalities exhibiting feelings of inadequacy, anxiety, disaffiliation, alienation and frustration or suffering from neurosis, psychosis or other mental disorders. Such persons are more susceptible to psychological dependence. Now, that is quite a broad statement to make, but I can assure you that no reputable doctor will dispute it.

Fourth, marihuana has no accepted medical use in modern medicine and serves no other purpose than to induce varying degrees of intoxication.

Fifth, marihuana has a growing attraction for the young and the adolescent.

May I parenthetically remind you that not too many years ago, there were those in high position who pooh-poohed the idea of danger of marihuana by saying it was a passing fad and would go away the same as goldfish swallowing. You know what has happened in the last few years.

Last, but perhaps most insignificant, although there is presently no scientific proof that continued use of marihuana will eventually cause permanent physical or mental injury, no one can guarantee that it will not. This is something they all agreed to.

The point which requires great emphasis is that, on the basis of these known and undisputed qualities, irrespective of any other disputed or unproven attributes, marihuana is harmful and dangerous to the user and to society.

Great harm is done when this phase of the problem is ignored by those who have access to public forums and who emphasize only the areas where there is some measure of disagreement or where scientific proof is lacking.

I do not have to remind you that the papers are filled with such statements but we do not have the proof. We have to have studies. We have to find out. They are talking about the permanent injury which may follow. It has taken us 20 or 30 years to find out in other matters. Basically, the areas where there is lacking scientific proof are these:

1. Does marihuana cause physical or psychological addiction?

2. Does it cause physical injury—physical, organic injury—as opposed to functional disorder?

By the way, as hard as it may seem to believe, heroin does not cause organic injury.

3. Does it lead to hard-core drugs?

4. Does it cause crime?

None of these questions can be answered with scientific proof presently available. In my opinion, with the exception of physical or organic injury, they can never be answered with scientific precision regardless of studies. And again, I am going to vacillate and say that those of you who are lawyers know exactly what I am talking about. The scientist exists on that phrase of his, "not necessarily." Which means you have to have perfection. The sociologist, the scientist, wants a perfect "with no exceptions." And they do not deal in probabilities the way lawyers do, the way courts do. What they are talking about is scientific proof. I say that it is absolutely impossible to get scientific proof acceptable to the sociologist or to the scientist that there is a correlation between marihuana use and crime. But, of course, with plenty of study and years of study, you can eventually establish whether or not marihuana does cause physical damage.

Now, by concentrating on these scientifically unproven areas, experts, unwittingly or otherwise, actually encourage experimentation with marihuana and even its habitual use, especially on the part of young people. It is this negative approach—the suggested lack of proof—which appeals to them, and they seize upon it as persuasive evidence that without such positive proof they may smoke marihuana with safety.

Examples of such gravely injurious statements appeared most recently in the news media. In a "letter to the editor" published in a Boston newspaper, someone who identified himself—he gave his name—as a clinical instructor in psychiatry at Harvard Medical School, in part, had the following to say—I have the newspaper clipping to show you:

> Marihuana is a mild drug, capable of giving many people mildly pleasant experiences. . . . (H)undreds of thousands of our bright and talented youth . . . occasionally use it in

a way essentially comparable (except legally) to having a
beer.

Further, in describing marihuana, he said:

> . . . (W)hat is known puts it (marihuana) in a category
> comparable to those other mild but not harmless drugs
> about which our society is ambivalent but far more toler-
> ant: alcohol, tobacco, caffeine.

In fairness to the young doctor, while delivering himself of
this rhetorical splurge he did say that marihuana is capable of
"doing some social and psychological harm to some users, probably especially to those teen-agers who use it in ways that help
avoid the necessary anxieties and tasks of growing up."

However, the harm caused by his unguided statement can't
be underestimated, especially because of his medical background and his association with a great university. Even as a
beginner in the field of psychiatry the author should have realized that the greatest impact on teen-agers would be his char-
acterization of marihuana as a "mildly pleasant experience"
and "essentially comparable . . . to having a beer." Very few of
these kids will consider themselves to be in the category of
those using marihuana to avoid the "necessary anxieties and
tasks of growing up." Many will construe the statement to
mean that it is okay to "light up"—"just like drinking beer," or,
as others have said, "no different than a couple of martinis."

I am sure that the author of the letter was well-intentioned
and meant to be objectively critical of the marihuana laws in
general. The manner of his approach and his use of words, to
me, indicated that he was unmindful of the harm his letter
could cause to the adolescent.

The point for emphasis is, of course, that youngsters are
extremely vulnerable to such a negative approach. Many will
seize upon his remarks as justification for experimenting with
or continued use of marihuana. Older people may well understand and weigh his remarks and make their own proper evaluation—as adults, but not the kids who read and hear about his
statement.

Another unfortunate example of this problem is a statement attributed by the news media to Dr. Roger O. Egeberg who was appointed recently to the post of Assistant Secretary for Health and Scientific Affairs. He is quoted as saying that marihuana is in the same category as alcohol and that the penalties for its possession and use are too stringent—more specifically (I quote), "If you send some guy to the penitentiary for 2 years because he's got a couple of sticks of marihuana on him, and then let an alcoholic go through a revolving door, there's something mixed up in our system. . . . Alcoholism remains our most serious problem . . . and there is a need for continuing study to determine long-range effects of marihuana."

By ignoring the known dangers of marihuana, Dr. Egeberg has committed a great disservice to the public, and his casual assessment of the problem is extremely unfair to the youngsters who need help and protection.

There is persuasive evidence that the greatest area of growth in the use of marihuana is between the ages of 14 and 18. In his position of importance and responsibility, Dr. Egeberg should utilize the powers of his office to protect these youngsters from exposure to anything which is mind-altering—whether it be marihuana or alcohol. Admittedly, there is a "need for continuing study to determine the long range effects of marihuana" as to permanent injuries it may cause. But this will require years to complete—hence of no immediate value in presently dealing with the great harm and danger these kids face now.

While it is true that there is no scientific and mathematical proof presently available that marihuana causes permanent, physical or mental harm, no one can question the danger inherent in the use of any mind-altering substance by youngsters whether it be alcohol, marihuana or glue sniffing.

The most ardent defenders of marihuana compare it to alcohol. They, of course, must agree that marihuana is an intoxicant. Let us therefore examine marihuana only on the basis that it is an intoxicant, without more (comment), and consider the possible harm and danger it may cause, not only to the user but to the public as well.

There is much to learn from society's generations of exposure to alcohol and tobacco. Both drugs are harmful and dangerous and, in some ways, perhaps even more so than marihuana. It has taken decades of vast, in-depth studies to demonstrate that grave consequences may result from cigarette smoking. Yet, in spite of the constant warnings by the Government—we hear it on TV and radio every minute of the day—by the American Cancer Society and other responsible groups concerning its danger, the use of tobacco continues to increase. The reason? It has become part of our culture—irreversibly and permanently.

Consumption of alcohol is associated with 50 percent of our crimes of violence and with 26,500 to 37,100 deaths and substantially over a million serious injuries on the highways annually. Alcohol has reduced millions of our fellow citizens to the status of mere vegetables, has wrecked countless thousands of homes and careers. Its use cannot be eliminated and its abuse cannot be controlled. The reason? Generations of use have made alcohol part of our culture—irreversibly and permanently.

At some point in the debate concerning marihuana we must pause, reflect and determine whether society can afford, in addition to the problems created by alcohol and tobacco, still another culture which would inflict, perhaps, even greater harm and danger—irreversibly and permanently.

The other day we learned through the news media, and this is again within a few days, that Federal investigators have found that alcohol was the major cause of 45 fatal aircraft accidents last year, all involving private pilots. This is considered a conservative figure. The Federal Aviation Administration's leading expert on the matter believes that as many as 200 of the Nation's 692 fatal private plane accidents in 1968 were caused by pilots numbed by the effects of alcohol.

There is an increasing body of considered opinion that marihuana (and other drugs) are causally related to many accidents of every description but go undetected. Courts everywhere are aware of this problem in connection with criminal activity. On many occasions police have testified before me that the accused didn't look or act right—but that he didn't stagger or smell of liquor; therefore, he concluded that he was not under the influence of liquor, but he was under the influence of something else.

The person who breaks the law or is guilty of misconduct

while under the influence of liquor can usually be detected. The abuse of alcohol can readily be ascertained. In the case of the dead pilots this was done by means of a blood test, and the same test can be utilized with the living.

I emphasize that, although alcohol and marihuana both cause intoxication and, in varying degrees, distort the ability to perceive time, distance and space, there is usually no diminution of muscular strength associated with marihuana.

This means that the person under the influence of marihuana is intoxicated but he does not sway or stagger. Physically, he is able to drive a car, pilot an airplane, operate machines, go about his business in a factory, in a school or anywhere and by reason of his mental disorientation inflict harm to himself and to others. The cause of the accident cannot be identified. Those who advise that marihuana is no worse than alcohol and that it poses no greater danger should pause and reflect on this—especially if they advocate its legalization and regulation.

The analogy is not, of course, perfect, but the fact is that the law recognizes the difference between an unmasked robber and one who hides his identity behind a mask. The latter is subject to a much stiffer sentence.

I repeat what I have said on other occasions. Of all the dangers inherent in the accelerating use of marihuana, I am fully persuaded that the greatest danger lies in the possibility of its being legalized and regulated. Just think for a moment as to what could happen if marihuana comes into general use through its legalization and regulation. Now that marihuana can be synthesized, we could expect a superior and greater ingredient equivalent to 100-proof liquor. Getting "high" or intoxicated would be possible for every man, woman, and child—at any time—anywhere—by simply lighting up. It would not be necessary to go home or to a bar. The ingredients for intoxication could be carried in every pocket or purse to be used at school, at work, in a motor vehicle, in an airplane, in public transportation, on the streets, in hospitals, in our restaurants, in our football and baseball and other sports activities, and on ad infinitum.

I will conclude with a rhetorical question: Does anyone seriously question whether we could survive the intolerable conditions that a marihuana culture would inflict upon society?

The answer should be obvious. And yet it is doubtful whether the best brains on Madison Avenue could plan a better campaign to develop such a culture than one which would start by brainwashing our youth.

Whether they realize it or not, the Harvard instructor and Dr. Egeberg and others who minimize the dangers of marihuana are definitely traveling this most dangerous path. Perhaps they should reflect on a statement contained in the September 26 issue of *Time* magazine—I think it is the last issue—quoting a tobacco company executive as saying, "A cigarette concern would have to be pretty stupid if it weren't looking into marihuana."

Speed: The Risk You Run

Testimony of Sidney Cohen,* M.D.,
Director of the Division of Narcotic Addiction and Drug Abuse,
National Institute of Mental Health, before the House Select Committee
on Crime, November 18, 1969.

DR. COHEN. Mr. Chairman, because of the brief period between your invitation to appear and the date of this hearing, it has not been possible for me to obtain clearance for this statement from the National Institute of Mental Health or from the Department of Health, Education, and Welfare. Therefore, it must not be considered either as a statement of policy, or as a representation of any viewpoint but my own.

It is really a pleasure to be here as one who may be qualified to assist in your consideration of the stimulant use-abuse pattern. I know that you have had a number of experts testify before you on this issue. Therefore, it is unnecessary for me to include in my remarks much of what already has been said. In order not to be misunderstood, however, it is desirable to note briefly some points upon which my position is based.

We are observing the misuse of the many amphetamines today. These drugs belong to the larger class of stimulants. Certain

---

*Dr. Cohen has been active in drug research for the past twenty years. His recent books include: The Beyond Within: The LSD Story; LSD; and The Drug Dilemma.

other stimulants which are not amphetamines are also capable of abuse so that the nonamphetamine stimulants should be included in your deliberations.

I am referring to drugs such as methyphenidate, Ritalin. These, too, have potential for abuse.

MR. PEPPER. *(Representative Claude Pepper, Dem.-Fla., Chairman). What are they?*

DR. COHEN. Ritalin is the trade name. Methyphenidate is the generic name. I would estimate, at least in some parts of the country, a certain degree of abuse of a drug like Ritalin.

Another point which must be made is that a broad spectrum of the abuse pattern of amphetamines is obvious. At one end is the person who will infrequently take an amphetamine to temporarily exceed his physiologic limits: to stay awake, to study for an exam, to drive through the night, to excel in an athletic contest. This sort of misuse is trivial in comparison to what is happening at the other end of the scale, but it must be mentioned since a rare disaster has occurred even under this minimal type of misuse.

I am referring here to the fact that there have been occasional deaths reported in connection with the use of amphetamines during athletic contests.

A second form of abuse is that of the person who regularly takes amphetamines without supervision. The amount used is either within average limits or is gradually increased to more than ordinarily prescribed amounts. A typical example of such an instance is the person who is given amphetamines for obesity, but who continues to use them long after any attempt to lose weight has been abandoned.

A third, and most extreme abuse of amphetamines is the swallowing of handfuls of pills, the "snorting" of amphetamine powder, or its injection into a vein in the form of a solution. Generally, the progression is from swallowing and sniffing to intravenous injection. The drug most frequently used in this country for this purpose is methamphetamine—speed, crystal, and meth. Other amphetamines can be similarly used; in fact, the one popular in Sweden for this purpose is phenmetrazine, also known as Preludin. You have already heard testimony concerning the effects of injecting huge amounts of "speed" and of the "speed-freak." I will simply mention that in certain respects it is, as you said in your opening statement, a more ominous practice than "mainlining" heroin. Furthermore, the use of hundreds of times the average dose of amphetamines is physically addicting, meaning that tolerance builds up, and definite withdrawal symptoms occur when the drug is discontinued.

You have already heard enough of the horror stories about the "speed-freak." Unfortunately, they are true. The panic and the paranoid states, the malnutrition, the prolonged nervous breakdowns, the infections that occur—all of these are well documented. I would like to mention one other complication that has been largely ignored—the possibility that the use of very high doses of amphetamines over long periods of time may lead to brain cell changes. This has been demonstrated in animals, and from the Japanese experience, in man. I have seen a few heavy users who, while not on any drug, were confused, had memory gaps, were apathetic, and partially disoriented. These are signs of organic brain damage. These are not features associated with a psychotic breakdown. That condition produces other kinds of symptoms.

It is my understanding that this committee is particularly interested in questions dealing with the relationship between the legitimate medical use and the illicit use of amphetamines, questions of control of supplies, diversion, and whether sufficient medical indications exist to permit their retention in view of our abuse problems. Others are better qualified than I to deal with some of these matters. I would prefer to contribute in those particular areas in which I may have some special knowledge.

One item that requires an answer is: How much of the licit supplies manufactured in this country find their way into illicit channels? I believe a real distinction must be made at this point between the ethical pharmaceutical firms who strictly control their amphetamine preparations, and the many other firms who make little or no effort to be sure that their products do not leak out into nonmedical channels. Although amphetamines originating from the plants of ethical manufacturers are occasionally seen on the street, most often the products of the dozens of less-than-scrupulous manufacturers, wholesalers, and distributors are on sale there—meaning the street. Barrels of amphetamines can be purchased today from these supply houses. In general, a considerable tightening up of the controls for the distribution of amphetamines and barbiturates is required at this time.

The physician who does not carefully supervise the patient for whom he has prescribed stimulants may be producing more trouble than he set out to cure. Good medical practice requires that the amphetamines not be given for prolonged periods except in the treatment of such infrequent patients as the narcoleptic or the hyperkinetic child.

MR. PEPPER. *What does that mean, Doctor?*

DR.COHEN. Narcolepsy is an infrequent condition in which the individual has a compulsion to fall asleep during his so-called waking period. He may fall asleep hundreds of times a day, and this is irresistible, and it can be successfully treated with amphetamines.

The hyperkinetic child is usually a youngster, perhaps with brain damage, perhaps not, who is behaviorally disordered, very hyperactive. For some strange reason, although you would think amphetamines would make him worse, it does improve the behavior of some of these children.

The ethical pharmacist should comply with the physician's refilling instructions and with the statutory regulations regarding refilling prescriptions for amphetamines. The interminable honoring of an old prescription for stimulants can be a source of abused supplies.

The medicine cabinet may be a Pandora's box which can be opened by young and old alike to enter into a career of drug abuse. It should not become a medical stockpile; rather, it should be regularly inspected to remove no longer needed medications.

Should the medical use of the stimulants be restricted only to special cases? I would be in favor of this if I were convinced that it would decrease the abuse of these drugs. It must be kept in mind, however, that the crystalline methamphetamine which is sniffed or injected intravenously is almost invariably made in clandestine laboratories. The manufacture of methamphetamine and dextroamphetamine is not difficult from precursors that are obtained in chemical supply houses. I hope that the sale of these precursors is being checked.

Clandestine laboratories which manufacture methamphetamine capsules and tablets have been detected during the past 3 years. If the entire licit production were curtailed, then more of these laboratories will spring up. Many foreign countries continue to be an easy source of supply for smugglers. Unless international regulation of the amphetamines can be initiated, this substance will remain in good supply even if medical uses of amphetamines were limited by law.

One type of amphetamine abuse might be decreased by restriction of the drug in the practice of medicine. This is exemplified by the patient who comes to depend upon her weight reduction pills. Unless the entire health profession regulates itself, then compulsory legislation of the amphetamines will come to pass.

I would hope that [doctors] would think about alternatives to weight reduction, which is an important medical problem, other than the use of pills, especially the overuse of pills. This is certainly, I think, a part of good medical practice.

MR. PEPPER. *What is the physical impact, what does the amphetamine contribute to weight reduction?*

DR. COHEN. The amphetamines alter the appetite-regulating center in the brain. It gives the individual a feeling of nonhunger, and in that way, appetite is reduced.

To carelessly prescribe amphetamines for trivial reasons by a few will result in the enactment of restrictive laws for all physicians.

Perhaps we can learn something about our amphetamine problem from the Japanese and Swedish experiences. After World War II in Japan, stocks of methamphetamine were dumped on the open market. Because of the postwar mental depression, and the need to work exceedingly long hours, an epidemic of amphetamine abuse swept over the country. This culminated 15 years ago when as many as 4 percent of the adult population in Japan's large cities were dependent on amphetamines. Strict controls over the availability of the stimulants, education of the populace and increased punitive action against those involved in the traffic produced considerable improvement in the situation. However, Japan is right now experiencing a resurgence in excessive amphetamine and other drug-taking.

Ten years ago an amphetamine called phenmetrazine was introduced into Sweden as a nonhabit forming, antiobesity pill. Its use was taken up by thousands, and eventually some crushed the tablets, dissolved them and injected them into their veins. It is estimated that 10,000 people in Sweden during 1968 used intravenous amphetamines. Sweden has a population of 8 million people.

During the past decade, the laws were made more and more stringent but without significant effect. Early in 1968 patients could have amphetamines prescribed only if their doctors applied to a special medical group for approval. This has not yet controlled the use of phenmetrazine because it is being illegally manufactured in that country, and because it is being smuggled in from other lands.

I know of no simple and easy answer to the amphetamine abuse problem. Before amphetamines and other abused substances can come under control, a number of fundamental changes must occur among our children and among citizenry.

1. We must gain a new respect for all drugs and transmit this respect to our children. Surely, we are childlike in our thinking if we believe that chemicals will ever be a solution to our personal problems. They can temporarily dissolve them, but never resolve them.

2. We must make these drugs as unavailable as possible, and deter major dealers with prompt and appropriate penalties.

3. Better goals which are relevant to the person, especially the young person, must be discovered. Much amphetamine-taking is due to boredom, lack of purpose, and existential alienation.

4. We must fight fire with fire. The ex-amphetamine abusers should be mobilized to "turn off" the users and prevent the spread of this epidemic. The person who has gone through the shattering life of the "speed-freak" is well equipped to understand and communicate with those who are involved with amphetamines.

5. An expanded education-information program will help de-

ter many from amphetamine excesses. Today we have sufficient reliable information about the dangers at hand to deter all but the very disturbed person from becoming caught in the amphetamine orbit that has as many downs as it has ups, and it all too often ends nowhere.

MR. PEPPER. *Doctor, you have told us what some of the medical uses of amphetamines are, that is, reducing obesity. Are there other medical uses that are legitimate?*

DR. COHEN. Yes, sir. I would think most medical doctors use amphetamines not only for the treatment of obesity, the narcoleptic individual, or the hyperkinetic child, but also for the fatigued person and for the individual with a mild depression. We know now that amphetamines are not effective in the treatment of severe or even moderate depressions, but for mild depressions, they may sometimes give enough of a lift to help a person through. Whether these are very realistic indications for their use, I hesitate to say. I think they do help some people. Other people are not helped, and still others get overinvolved in the use of their stimulant prescription.

MR. PEPPER. *It may be that we should stimulate the drug industry to create new drugs that would not have the bad effects of these amphetamines but would still have a similar medicinal purpose. Is that a good suggestion?*

DR. COHEN. I think your suggestion is a very rational one. For example, I can visualize from a neurophysiologic point of view—that is, from my understanding of how the brain functions, I can visualize that we can obtain a substance which reduces the feeling of hunger and yet will not stimulate. So that, yes, this would be a possibility for our pharmaceutical firms to work on.

MR. PEPPER. *Doctor, what's the approximate incidence of narcolepsy and of hyperkinetic problems?*

DR. COHEN. It is very low, very low.

MR. PEPPER. *So there is not a great demand?*

DR. COHEN. No, the billions of tablets that have been manufactured go elsewhere. When I was in Sweden, just one year ago, I asked the same question and they said that in Stockholm they have only approved six prescriptions for this purpose. So, this is a minimal use of the drug.

MR. PEPPER. *Now, does tolerance develop during the use of amphetamines for weight control?*

DR. COHEN. It can. It does not necessarily have to, but it can. I know of incidences where people kept increasing the dose not so much for weight control, but because they did not get a lift out of the drug, and they increased the amount over and above what the doctor ordered.

MR. PEPPER. *Have you noticed any higher incidence of requests for amphetamines at student health services with which you have been in contact?*

DR. COHEN. I have spoken to people who work at the student health services and there is some degree of interest and desire to obtain supplies of these drugs.

MR. PEPPER. *What is your observation as to whether doctors are becoming more or less disposed to prescribe these methamphetamines and amphetamines?*

DR. COHEN. I am not qualified to answer that, but my impression is that I think they are beginning to realize that these are not trivial drugs. Perhaps some of the other witnesses can help with that question.

MR. PEPPER. *Just for the record, will you describe what is methamphetamine and what is an amphetamine?*

DR. COHEN. Yes, sir. Amphetamines are a group of drugs which, as I mentioned in my remarks, are called stimulants. There are other drugs which are stimulants—cocaine, Ritalin—but amphetamines are the largest group of stimulants.

Now, amphetamines are many drugs. There may be dozens of amphetamines. One is methamphetamine, another is dextroamphetamine, another one is Benzedrine. These are three and there are still others. When we speak of methamphetamine, we are speaking of an amphetamine.

MR. PEPPER. *Besides the contribution that they make, perhaps, to the reduction of obesity by diminishing the appetite, and besides the narcoleptic and the hyperkinetic instances, and their use, you said, perhaps for mild depression, are there other legitimate medical uses for these drugs?*

DR. COHEN. One that comes to mind is the treatment of the tired person, the person who is always worn out, can't get going in the morning, and so forth, or the person who is overfatigued. This is one use to which the amphetamines are not infrequently put.

MR. PEPPER. *You mentioned a while ago the tendency to take a handful of these drugs. I heard the other day somebody telling about it becoming more and more the habit of truckdrivers to take a handful of these things and swallow them with water, sometimes without knowing the strength of the particular drug that they took. Have you heard of instances like that?*

DR. COHEN. Yes. This is so common that the source of supply of many of these amphetamines is at truck stops, where they can be purchased. One of these drugs is called the Los Angeles turnaround. If you take enough of them, you can drive from New York to Los Angeles and back without stopping.

Now, it is pretty obvious that if one does not sleep for a period of days, keeps awake on pills, his judgment is going to be impaired, and this has happened. There have been more truck accidents occurring because people either dozed off for a moment while driving, trying to keep going, or actually had hallucinations as a result of taking a lot of amphetamines. This is one of the complications of amphetamines.

MR. PEPPER. *Can the person who takes a large quantity of these drugs experience a high?*

DR. COHEN. Yes, sir. This is why it is a drug of abuse among many people. It is for the experience of the high. And this is more particularly the reason why it is being injected, because the high is a tremendous, as they call it, a "rush" or "flash." It is a high very reminiscent of the cocaine high.

MR. PEPPER. *How many of these tablets would ordinarily be required for one to experience a high?*

DR. COHEN. That depends on the individual. I recall taking a single 5 milligram tablet of dextroamphetamine and I was high and jittery for about 8 hours.

On the other hand, other individuals, especially if they have been taking them over a period of time, can take hundreds of milligrams at a time in order to get that same high.

MR. PEPPER. *Now, do you happen to know what these drugs sell for, if they sell in the street, these tablets?*

DR. COHEN. No; I am not familiar with the current quotations on them. Actually, they should be very inexpensive. They are easily made and I heard awhile back that one could pick them up for a dime or so, but maybe the price has gone up.

MR. PEPPER. *In our hearings in San Francisco, there were 13 bins of amphetamines somewhat like Benzedrine, as I recall, that had 1,200,000 of them, and they were consigned by a manufacturer in Chicago to a consignee in Tijuana, Mexico. The Federal Bureau of Narcotic Addiction and Drug Abuse acting on information furnished by our committee staff checked up on it, and they found that the address of the so-called consignee was the 11th hole of the golf course at Tijuana and that a customs broker had diverted these amphetamines at the border into the black market. As I recall the hearing, the figure was 25 cents apiece that they were being sold for in the black market.*

You did say that amphetamines and methamphetamines are hallucinogenic?

DR. COHEN. They can, especially when taken in the large amounts that they are taken in today, produce hallucinations, delusions, and, what is very ominous, a state of suspiciousness, of oversuspiciousness, called paranoia, which leads them into activities that can harm themselves and others.

MR. PEPPER. *Is the effect of taking these amphetamines by injection different from taking them orally? I mean is the effect different?*

DR. COHEN. Yes, not only do the effects start quicker, but the high is higher and one loses control more easily.

Now, as soon as one feels oneself coming down, then one re-injects, so that one is really going on a speed binge. This can go on for days, perhaps over a week. During this period, one does not eat. You see, it is an appetite suppressant. And one rarely sleeps because it is used as an antifatigue substance.

MR. PEPPER. *That is what we popularly know as "speed"?*

DR. COHEN. Methamphetamine.

MR. PEPPER. *And LSD is——*

DR. COHEN. That is a little different group. It is in the group of hallucinogens, although I would like to clear up one point, namely, that the large doses of methamphetamine can produce all the hallucinations and all the strange illusions and delusions that LSD can do, even though they are two different groups of chemicals.

MR. PEPPER. *Under the Narcotics Rehabilitation Act, can persons be treated who have become abusers of methamphetamine and amphetamines, or is the treatment under that Act limited to heroin users?*

DR. COHEN. The legislation says those who are addicted to narcotics or potentially addicted to narcotics, and I would interpret that as meaning people who are involved, overinvolved with drugs like methamphetamine and who are——

Mr. Pepper. *You think they could be treated?*

Dr. Cohen. They could.

Mr. Pepper. *Along with the heroin addict?*

Dr. Cohen. Although perhaps the legislation could be more specifically written.

Mr. Pepper. *Doctor, according to your observation, who are the principal abusers of these amphetamines and methamphetamines, by sex and race and age, if you have any knowledge of them?*

Dr. Cohen. The present epidemic, especially the use of injectable amphetamines, is a white middle class-upper class phenomenon. These are people who are bored, frustrated, have no particular requirement to support themselves, and so forth. These are the ones who are getting into trouble.

CHAPTER THIRTEEN

A Psychiatrist Looks at LSD

By Daniel X. Freedman,* M.D.
Professor and Chairman, Department of Psychiatry,
University of Chicago

While extensive drug-taking of all kinds is a general social issue, it would aid rational judgment to separate the problems inherent in the different categories of drugs which are abused. The sedatives (including alcohol, barbiturates, and certain so-called minor tranquilizers) as well as the narcotics (opium and its derivatives such as morphine, codeine and heroin) may be technically addicting. Persons can organize their lives so that the procurement of such drugs becomes of overriding importance (they are "habituated"), and upon withdrawal there are physiological symptoms which produce discomfort and symptoms which can be modified by another dose of drugs. Narcotics, especially, produce marked tolerance, such that larger doses are required for similar subjective effects; with larger dosage the withdrawal syndrome will be more

---

*Reprinted from *Federal Probation,* June 1968.

Since 1960, Dr. Freedman has studied various drugs and their effects for the National Institute of Mental Health, and from 1966-68 he was chairman of the National Academy of Sciences' Panel on Psychiatric Drugs. In his research, he has concentrated on the effects of LSD, mescaline and other psychedelics upon the brain and on behavior.

severe.

Other potentially dangerous drugs can be habitually abused. These are the excitants such as amphetamine, methadrine ("speed"), and cocaine; hallucinogens, such as LSD, STP, psilocybin, DMT, and mescaline; the delirium-producing drugs such as belladonna derivatives (atropine, scopolamine); various intoxicants such as benzine-containing compounds (glue and gasoline); anesthetics such as ether; and substances more difficult to classify, such as large dosages of nutmeg. Marihuana has sedative and euphoriant properties and in high dosage or with potent extracts, psychotomimetic effects. All of these drugs variably alter subjective states and have been abused. Each presents a variety of specific problems and risks. Many, on the other hand (including LSD) have been appropriately used. Alcohol is the most prevalently abused (and associated with crimes of violence); it is followed by the barbiturates, mild tranquilizers, amphetamines, marihuana, and then the opiate narcotics. The hallucinogens are a rather new addition to this catalogue of "goofogenic" agents.

Psychedelic Effects

History records a variety of substances derived from plants which can produce strange subjective states. Certain of these drugs are repeatedly cited as leading to "learning" or revelation; often they are involved in some mystical or ritual use. These drugs reveal normally suppressed components of our experience, vividly exposing them to our attention. They produce a heightened experience of any sensory input, a heightened sense of clarity but a diminished control over what is being experienced. Humphrey Osmond coined for these drugs the term "psychedelic" to mean "mind-manifesting."

The fact that a certain class of drugs so sharply compels this level of function for a chemically determined package of time has intrigued scientists who search for the mechanisms by which the brain can so be altered. This intense subjective experience presents a startling contrast to ordinary reality. Our minds are apparently capable of viewing the world in terms of "portentousness"; the slightest sensation becomes laden with meaning. Meaningfulness becomes more important than the object that is meant, redness that is more important than the object that is red. Qualities and sensations gain a life of their own. The sense of truth is experienced as compellingly vivid but not the inclination to test the truth of the senses! Thus, the drugs reveal an innate capacity of the mind to see more than it can tell, to experience more than it can explicate, to believe in and be more impressed by more than we can rationally justify, to experience "boundaryless-ness" events from the banal to the profound. These drugs reflect an innate capacity (like the dream) of which the *waking* mind is capable. The familiar and habitual now appear novel. Those habits and constancies with which we generally order the world around us into a sensible sequence now become less important, and items, elements, and aspects of our perceptual world now compel attention.

To this disjointed world of clear perceptions we can react with awe rather than tempered judgment or even with irrational boundless effect—ecstasy or terror. One can also react simply with a sense of surprise. Unlike the sleeping dreamer, the waking dreamer is confronted with two compelling and contradictory orders of reality—the interface of belief and the orderly rules of evidence. The trip back to reality after "tuning in" to this region may be discordant or harmonious; one's sense of both the inner and outer world may be revised in a healthy way or altered to suit the cosmic fantasies engendered in the drug state. For some, the experience is simply odd and interesting; for others it seems to reveal profound mysteries; and for almost anyone it represents a conflict with the reality the waking mind normally sees. From the wealth of normally useless perceptions *potentially* available to us, we generally select what is useful in order to make our way physically and socially in our world. This selective capacity tends to be diminished with these drugs and hence all experience is novel.

The particular *content* of the trip depends upon expectation, the individual's capacity to cope with the novel and the surrounding events. The way in which the drug-taking culture or groups try to make sense out of the experience in effect gives an overall direction to it. Music can absorb attention during the flux—the kaleidoscopic "internal T.V. show"—and guide one through the confusions of the trip; directing attention to the outside, to pleasant objects or thinking of "good" or high thoughts can also help.

Religion especially contains an apt language to describe the boundless, the infinite, the sense of belief which transcends proof. The part of the mind which is tapped by these drugs, the part that sees vivid and boundless images—a clear dream where barriers are transcended—also can underwrite hallucinatory experience and delusional belief; hence these are also called psychotomimetic drugs. Nor is it surprising that we should see a variety of confusional aftereffects including a tendency to overvalue the insights of the drug world without the corrections of experience and logic. Thus, these drugs do allow the mind to "expand" upon and vivify sensations; they "shrink" that part of the mind which exerts logical control.

The Dangers of LSD

Drugs such as LSD lure the unwary from the acquisition of competence. Not all persons who experiment fall for this lure. For the majority, the single drug experience may mean only a passing episode or temporary upset. For many it may simply provide interesting and enlightening (but unspecific) testimony into the orders of experience which our minds must normally or unconsciously integrate.

Adverse effects fall into four major groups. First, the bulk of harmful effects have turned out to be those visible and dramatic episodes of drug panic known as "the bad trip." The fact is, individuals cannot reliably control or predict exactly what experience they may have under the drug, and since their "anchors" to the familiar world are markedly loosened, they may easily be tripped into an escalating panic. The risk of this must at least be 10 percent for each single trip, a risk enhanced by high dosage, by unstable circumstances and by unstable motives (as well as by uncertain control over dosage because of black market manufacture). The less an individual is firmly and adaptively entrenched in a pattern of life, the less he has a reservoir of established habits and values, the more vulnerable he may be to a bad trip and to aftereffects. Accordingly, most panic reactions to an unpleasant trip are seen in people younger than 26 years of age. A really complete loss of judgment—psychotic behavior leading to suicide or homicide—is quite rare in LSD panic states.

In general, the effects of bad trips are short lasting (24 to 48 hours) and manageable by knowledgeable physicians in emergency rooms. Reassurance, perhaps the use of sedative or tranquilizing agents and brief followup after the panic appear to help. There is now a wider-spread understanding in the medical community of how to deal with various drug-related emergencies. This, in turn, leads to less off-the-cuff headline-making which then enhances panic on the part of patients, friends, and inexperienced medical staff. To an extent, bad trips can even be managed by those lay guides and "friends" who are able to provide appropriate calm reassurance.

A second common group of transient adverse effects—after-effects—are the variable mood changes, the perplexities, "flashbacks," and confusions seen after one or several good or bad trips.

Third, after single or several doses the drug can be a catalyst for those who are already psychotic or those who—without luck or timely intervention—are about to be overtly so. This is a quite small group. The overall incidence of psychosis has not increased in this country because of LSD, but too often it is the vulnerable who tend to experiment.

Finally, there are serious effects of too many "good trips." For a small but visible subculture using LSD, the drug can reinforce retreat from productivity and an insidious pattern of retreat, passivity, mood changes, and impaired judgment and dropping out—an effect perhaps more damaging to personality organization than actual psychosis.

Data generated at the National Institute of Mental Health (demonstrating the increased scientific interest in the drug—a useful side effect of the publicity) indicate that some people in the drug state may pay attention to auditory frequencies they normally ignore and thereafter continue to be sensitive to those frequencies. This is a demonstration that after the drug some people tend to be able to hear and perhaps see the world somewhat differently than they once did; this fact in itself is neither beneficial nor harmful. It simply demonstrates that experiences during the drug state can, to varying degrees, influence subsequent modes of perceiving. Yet, this may happen without the "consent" of the subject; we see this in the publicized "flashback" or the unwanted trip without a drug which may be accompanied by varying degrees of panic or confusion. This is akin to the recurrent bad dream about an overwhelming experience—a traumatic experience which has not been mastered and for which the person was usually unprepared. Treatment with antianxiety drugs and brief psychotherapy generally suffices. While the mechanisms for this puzzling reaction are of basic interest to researchers, and while it may be quite upsetting, the effect is often more dramatic than dangerous.

For some people the reaction *after* the drug is a period of mild depression, perplexity, and a kind of passive giving-up. Because the drug clearly presents persons with a clash of realities—with two orders of reality (ordinary reality, and the tempting or confusing and limitless dream world of the drug)—young people may dwell upon the contrast and the disappointments which everyday life presents. In some, suicidal ideas or acts may develop; it ought to be recalled, however, that this is the third most common cause of death in the young adult age group with or without the aid of drugs.

Some tend to overvalue the omnipotence and untested personal insights arrived at in the drug state; they continue to retreat from everyday life seeking the vivid intangibles of the drug world. Others become self-absorbed and perplexed about the nature of life and reality. Such confusions—reinforced by drug subcultures—lead to moderately severe or quite major maladjustments as seen in the severely impaired dropout. Yet, we should remember that others can tap into this drug experience using it simply for escape or enlightenment; they do not mistake the visions of the drug world with specific plans or programs for everyday living.

Cultures surround drug taking, such as that of the pseudo-hippie. It is unkempt and unsightly, but occasionally functions to keep its members in some tenuous accord with reality. Because one loses his usual anchors to reality, he must lean upon others for structure and support; hence groups and cults naturally tend to form in order to link this strange experience to some kind of social reality. This is why I have called these drugs "cultogenic"; they enhance group formation. Highly structured religious rituals can both isolate and explain the intrinsically strange and novel drug experience, and do so in a fashion that does not lend to personal eccentricity and self-destructive flights from reality; this is evident in the Peyote religion. Similarly, under knowledge-able medical control, effects of the drug can be guided and managed with a low risk of harm.

If we take a good hard look at the national scene it is fortunate that there is still only a small group of dedicated long-term users of LSD and associated compounds. Apart from the rapidity with which some of this minority drop out of a competent role in school or society, I see little overall difference between their passivity, inappropriateness, and lack of engagement with the world and that which we have long observed. There are always such disturbed young people. In the past they had less socially acceptable (or passable) ways of retreating from the tasks of adulthood. Nevertheless, some observers of the chronic user believe that the sharp personality change, the notable passive receptivity to all varieties of excitement and stimuli, the magical thinking and the poor organization in the presence of a capacity for personal relationships cannot be explained solely on psycho-logical grounds. As yet, there is no solid evidence for brain damage in these cases; but they may indeed let the drug effects overwhelm their capacity for making distinctions and be unable to control sensory inputs. These people in any event clearly suffer from a hangover of too many "good trips"! The fact that appro-priately supervised "trips" in normal or quite sick people do not usually lead to anything which appears like lasting damage indi-cates that the persisting inability to suppress and disregard the flood of input is in part a consequence of the setting in which this potent drug is taken and the lack of structure-building ac-tivities and "training" after the trip. A setting which emphasizes constancy therapy or ritual supporting the logical mind would tend to retard this opening up and this passive and apparently uncritical acceptance of all stimuli—sometimes miscalled love by the pseudohippie. Yet, there are hints that passive acceptance, denial or diminution of aggressivity also occur in Peyote cultures. I believe we must look more closely at the whole issue of chronic use to understand it. Finally, we should note that angry prosely-tizing can follow chronic usage; here the user "turns out" tran-scending his own weaknesses by getting others to join him.

Scope of abuse of LSD

Several years ago I was of the opinion that LSD would be a drug which had certain fad qualities. After consultation with many knowledgeable colleagues and watching the problem quite closely, I believe this opinion was correct and that the *rapid* rate of increase of interest and untutored experimentation with LSD has clearly begun to decline. Government-supported research into this difficult area of the prevalence of drug-taking—including a wide number of common compounds—is underway and should, when completed, produce socially useful data.

We need more finely detailed studies which could show us how it is that "carriers" can introduce the drug into a small population, essentially advertise it (in terms of informal accounts of "fascinating" experiences), catching the attention of the curious, the passive, the tag-alongs, and the unwary and thereby seeding an episode of drug experimentation. This is not an unlikely pattern of contagion. I am quite aware that, after the traveling medicine shows come to campus (complete with unbearded but beaded gurus peddling drugs), there is an increase of drug experimentation reinforced by the notion that everyone who is "in" is doing it.

It has pleased me to notice that this increased interest can be temporary and at least on some campuses has dwindled. According to people with whom I have talked, this is because students could see the effects in friends who were dropping out or having hangups with the drug. In brief, gullibility *can* be followed by the exercise of observation and good judgment, as we might well expect it to be among the great majority of the sensible college-age population.

It has been distressing to see that some high school students, yearning for the fruits of maturity, have experimented with the drug. This has not reached the proportions of a monumental problem, yet it does require awareness and tact on the part of secondary school educators. The lurid but unproved dangers of fractured cromosomes and visions of a race of psychedelic monsters have probably discouraged many from experimenting.

With respect to the extent and pattern of usage, we should anticipate that history will repeat itself and that we will find some small enclaves on campuses (or in hippie cultures) in which

167

the drug will suddenly be discovered; a rash of experimentation will follow; a minority will become frequent users and someone will be in sufficiently visible personal trouble to begin to alert the gullible; the rate will then decline. So that the overall interest and facination in LSD seems now not to be increasing and in fact to be declining and localized to a hard core minority of experimenters who turn to other stimulants with avidity. The verdict on LSD given to me several years ago by a narcotic addict, "Man, that stuff is too risky," will eventually be a fairly prevalent view.

It is harder to discourage young people from experimenting by presenting the evidence for these risks than when they can "decide" the danger is to their physical health. The issue for the hard core is one's "right" to have subjective experiences and one can save face by giving up drugs on the grounds of damage to the body rather than accepting a supposed infringement of a civil right. The hard core minority of users characteristically deny the psychological risks in the face of overwhelming evidence, thereby demonstrating the poor judgment which the life of the drugged dropout entails.

In summary, the dangers of LSD, about which there can no longer be controversy, are the psychological and social dangers. These are the high risk or the lack of certainty as to outcome of a drug trip, and the availability of attraction of drugs to the unwary and unprepared. The drug presents a real psychological risk when taken by the wrong people at the wrong time for the wrong motive, e.g., young people in a personal "hangup" attempting to shortcut personal growth and decisions in a search for their "real" selves. The drug is tempting in this search for the "true self." Unfortunately, looking inside one's self under the drug simply further removes the subject from those anchors to reality which provide necessary guidelines for judgment. Unguided self-examination under the drug is a common cause of subsequent confusions and chronicity—a passive posture of dropping out can ensue; this can lead to a variety of clinical pictures. Temporary bad trips are the most frequent adverse effect and flashbacks present a puzzling though treatable issue. In general, the aftereffects "open up" individuals who then do not seem to be able to disregard or integrate magical thinking and inappropriate or maladaptive thought.

The psychedelic mystique

We should note the role of the drug mystique in spreading and supporting drug usage. LSD was huckstered by a pseudointellectual elite and the fact that the media focus sensational attention upon either harmful or remarkable effects is precisely equivalent to an advertising campaign.

This publicized mystique offers readymade structure, style and ideology with which a wide variety of confused and lost youngsters can rationalize their protean confusion. If the professions do not encourage drugs by overreaction or by covert sensational interest, we will have a long-range, useful effect on the contagion of drug experimentation. In any event the psychedelic gurus are in no position to have to take care of the consequences of what they so happily promise and initiate. As they seek advertisement for themselves through debates and lurid magazine articles, they are certain that they have a civil right to have a "private" experience. Yet they continue to publicize their private experiences, unmindful of the fact that society has to deal with the consequences. They announce—far in advance of actual widespread usage—the "inevitable" use of these drugs by the young. Thus they can enjoy declaring the establishment to be helpless and incite youth to revolt—all under the sanction of inevitability—a huckster's device to which the gullible still respond. Widespread epidemics of drug usage are neither inevitable nor do they inexorably require the severe counterreaction which hysterical legislators, in their fear and irritation, propose.

New drugs of abuse

As long as individuals can be lured into experimenting with their subjective feelings with drugs we will have some problem of abuse of these compounds. What is more difficult to convey to the young is that it really does take time for the experts to investigate a drug and that the extensive but imprecise knowledge and experience of lay pharmacologists and street corner laboratories are not a reliable training or a basis for sound, accurate and safe research.

There are now a number of synthesized compounds which are

similar in effects to LSD. Structurally related to mescaline—more precisely derivatives of amphetamine—drugs such as STP have been abused. Misinformation travels widely and quickly. Similar to the effects of LSD, some are shorter acting or less intense (STP, e.g.). Scientists are interested in the particular pattern of psychological effects which may be emphasized with one drug rather than another in the hope that they can both come to an understanding of the precise psychological systems affected and the hope that, with more precise control over drug states, their specific neurochemical basis can be investigated as well as potential therapeutic effects. The drugs may be "tracers" leading to those brain systems which may be altered in mental disorders.

A small minority of drug users, frustrated with problems attendant upon psychedelic drugs, have turned to other amphetamine derivatives such as methedrine ("speed") which tend to produce a keyed-up mental and physical state rather than psychedelic effects; somewhat similar to cocaine's effects, methedrine can be associated with paranoid perceptions and an urge toward action which in the wrong circumstances can lead to violence. Overdose can be physically dangerous.

Certainly among the dedicated minority of indiscriminate drug experimenters turning from one to aonther drug in search for kicks, one could anticipate histories in which the experimental if not addictive use of narcotics might be involved. This is simply to point out that a dedicated career of drug-taking and a preoccupation with underground sources of drugs can lead a quite small and insignificant minority to a thoroughly indiscriminate pattern of experimentation. It does not mean that the use of LSD inevitably leads to the use of any single other drug, narcotic or not. Nor is it true that marihuana inevitably leads to heroin; we should not confuse arrangements of the marketplace with the primary drug effect.

The fact that underground purveyors of narcotics may peddle marihuana and that the law treats both classes of drugs as equally dangerous is far more relevant. It may, however, be true that indiscriminate drug experimentation is enhanced by the habit of "turning on" with drugs. Yet it is quite evident that this subjective experience in itself does not compel drug experimentation; indeed, the majority of narcotics users probably first tried alcohol.

It is also true that there are far more users of marihuana than there are narcotics addicts. The use of this agent has spread in the presence of very severe legal sanctions since 1937.

Genetic dangers

Recently the focus of interest on the harmful effects of LSD has shifted to observation of changes in the genetic apparatus of the white cells of the blood. Drugs can be added to a suspension of these cells. After a period of time the cultured cells are viewed under the microscope, and the chromosomal apparatus is examined and classified. This is a time-consuming method, expensive because of the laboratory technicians required. A number of laboratories are now studying these phenomena, yet headlines about the effects of LSD—"fractured chromosomes"—did not indicate that such common substances as caffeine, aspirin and certain drugs used daily in obstetrics can also produce test tube changes of the same kind and frequency as LSD. They did not indicate that the effect of LSD in the test tube (let alone the effect of LSD on the white cells of the drug user) is not at all consistent. Nor has it been stressed that some laboratories cannot even identify an abnormal frequency of fractured chromosomes in drug users. Thus, the test tube reactions with lymphocytes derived from different persons are not uniform; reactions which *are* found, occur with a number of drugs, and the white cells of drug users produce quite variable results. Finally, fractured chromosomes are not a disease but a laboratory observation and the significance of this partly subjectively evaluated laboratory finding to human well-being is quite elusive.

Nor has the series of psychotomimetic drugs been tested to see if it is this property of such molecules—their ability to produce a visionary state—which can fracture chromosomes. Finally, the truly genetic significance of drug effects when they do occur is a matter of guilt by association—the observation that chromosomal changes can be produced by some agents which may produce a higher risk of cancer (but also by agents which may be useful in the chemotherapy of cancer). Radiation and certain viral infections also can produce chromosomal changes. The duration of changes with these various agents is uncertain. Almost any drug given at the right time during gestation and in the right

dosage can produce stillbirths and stunted growth in experimental animals with or without fractured chromosomes. There
is no data as yet that LSD is a reliably good teratogen (such as
thalidomide), nor is there any necessary biological link between
fractured chromosomes in white cells of mother and/or child
and birth defects; these usually occur quite independently.

In summary, there has been interesting and highly suggestive
(and highly sensationalized) research, none of which indicates
directly that LSD damages human germ cells (which incidentally,
if damaged, have a poor chance of forming life). Such laboratory
findings should raise the level of suspicion and provoke research.
This has happened but the data as yet are hardly convincing
when extrapolated to the risk of human disease or deformity.
Neither European nor American experience in over 20 years of
LSD research nor the data of ethnology have pointed to such
problems.

None of us—if we intend to put up with a world in which
drugs are manufactured and distributed—has any business expecting that any drug will be without harm to anyone at any time.
Prudence has always counseled that in pregnancy, especially in
the first trimester, the intake of drugs should be carefully moni-
tored. Thus, whether or not these findings have any relevance to
health or reproduction, their publication has cast a pall on the
omnipotent notion that one can experiment without risk. It has
offended the expectation of youth that there was a drug which
was their "right" to take with impunity. They expected parental
rather than biological recrimination!

Educational lapses

Parenthetically, it is striking that high school and college
science curricula do not contain up-to-date experiments and information on drugs generally. Few social science courses offered
to this age group stress the history of salvationist movements, of
fads, or the psychology of influence as represented by advertising
in its various forms (including that which provokes social and
ideological fads and fashions). Both issues are relevant to preventive measures which might be effective. Considering the fact that
LSD was 22 years old before it was widely abused and that it was
largely among highly educated people that the LSD fad was prop-

agandized, it is striking that philosophers and literary experts, that students of man's struggle to bring the irrational and rational components of experience into accord, did not speak up. To put it briefly, there was a strange lapse on the part of those who knew better and failed to confront the inadequate psychology, trite philosophy, and uninformed posturing of the psychedelic poseurs. Perhaps they felt that the drug experience presented something unique, new and novel to society, a fact refuted by anthropology and pharmacology.

In any event, pharmacology represents the application of a number of basic science disciplines to the question of the mode of action of drugs and their effect on bodily systems. Generally, this is a graduate school specialty which has to be taught to all medical students and to Ph.D. candidates in biomedical sciences; a practical course is given to nursing and pharmacy students. I believe that some support for the development of educational tools and a revision of high school texts would be most useful not only so that students can understand how any drug is developed, manufactured, and tested but so that they can understand something about the scientific issues and the difficulties in weighing risk and gain in applying drugs.

We cannot afford educated leaders who believe that drugs are hatched by a conspiracy of money-mad pharmaceutical manufacturers, or on the other hand, that the drugs are unadulterated magic bullets capable of precisely manipulating any desired mental or physical state. These misunderstandings are evidence of "two cultures" and lurk in the background of all of our concerns about contemporary problems in the use and abuse of all drugs. Throughout history man has responded to drugs with the basic notion of their potency—either the possibility of enhancing physical strength or sexual potency, or of harming and poisoning. These universal irrational notions are easily tapped, impairing effective judgment of legislators as well as medical men.

The motives for drug use

The motives for experimenting with drugs are hard to pin down. Many factors are at work. Our society is mobile, and acting up is a ready substitute for isolation, depression, and mild despair. Many college students who have experimented with these agents seem to have an intense need to feel. They use drugs in order to establish a hitherto elusive contact with themselves and others. The seductive ease with which one can instantly change his normal expectations and experience is a lure for others. The prolonged period in which the slow and painful acquisition of competence is demanded from an intrinsically impatient age group also plays a role.

Curiosity about the mind, about what can be experienced and knowing about who one is and is to be, can be expected. All the crises of adolescence—the fluidity, shifts of rules, and expectations and search for identity—play into the drug-taking culture. Parents can be defied as the frustration of years of inexperience are reversed by an intense, drug-induced, subjective experience which parents have not had.

This is a risk-taking age in which many can be dared by accounts of psychedelic experiences. They see the drug as an emotional fitness test. They experiment with control; they like to drink and test their ability to stop; they debate whether to smoke or not, masturbate or not, or to study. In general, they are rehearsing their strengths and autonomy at a time when their lives are, in fact, largely unwritten. They probe for consequences and impatiently leap the barriers of time to come to grips with life and seize the fruits and risks promised in the future. These motives may underlie many of the grimmer statistics of the 18 to 25 age group committing accidents and suicide. One wonders if these represent the inevitable costs of learning the lesson of consequences of limits, of mortality.

Whatever the personality needs of drug takers may be, this is an age group which is "changing its skin," impatient to leap from the present moment into the unknown and untested future. Whatever sustains their episodes of drug-taking has to be matched against all the forces in contemporary life which tend to make the future bleak and structureless, which fail to underwrite periods of transition and to reward competences as they are in fact, acquired. Affluence and privilege can be accompanied by a lack of challenge and genuine investment; on the other hand helplessness in controlling the environment can enhance the value of experimenting with the internal environment. All these factors have and can be cited as enhancing drug-taking. Although the majority of our youths do not even experiment with these drugs, I find explanations of the differences between American and European use still not satisfactorily explained, and the facts still elusive when we seek for accountable factors.

Laws

It is a crime to possess marihuana and to manufacture or distribute LSD. Neither marihuana nor LSD directly induce or incite criminal behavior. Yet current legislative proposals will now make criminals out of the foolish who possess LSD and other such drugs thus putting possessors in the same class as those criminals who manufacture and distribute agents which are potentially toxic. Another law, the Rogers Bill (H.R. 14096), would "rehabilitate" those so arrested although the bulk of users are not sick nor are they chronic users of LSD. This—plus a proposed doubling of agents, and the recent administrative removal of the Bureau of Drug Abuse Control from the scientifically informed Food and Drug Administration to the Department of Justice where policing of narcotics and all dangerous drugs is being amalgamated—at a time when medical experts generally agree that LSD use is declining! Perhaps these laws will eliminate long hair, bare feet and beads, but the proposed legislation is not discriminating and specific nor based on sound information, and the recent administrative consolidation may isolate enforcement personnel and policies from the medical, scientific and educational advice available and may bring all drug-abuse control under the same suspect advice which has in the past amalgamated marihuana and opiates as offenses. Some day federal legislation preempting the states should be arrived at after due reflection and sound evaluation of available information.

Marihuana is derived from the plant which produces hemp, the flowering tops of which are smoked for a "high." The resinous materials which can be expressed from the plant have been made into potent hashish cakes. This material can be obtained only from the plants grown in the Near or Far East or North Africa. Scientists have just begun to gain chemical control over the wide variety of constituents found in the plant, and to identify molecules which produce the characteristic effects. Standard materials are required and a far greater synthesis of the active molecules before appropriate comparative studies can be undertaken. The potent forms of marihuana produce momentary paranoid states. The potent preparations of the East when taken over a long term in excess reportedly produce social patterns not unlike that of our own skid row. The mild marihuana available in this country probably ranges in potency from that of banana peel to moderately effective material.

I do not find it possible at this juncture to advise the legalization of marihuana as some proponents argue; potential dangers need to be assessed. I also believe it takes time for a society to learn how to orient to the drugs it uses in order to provide customs and safeguards around ingestion patterns. We have hardly done this for alcohol. While there is no evidence of harmful physical effects of the marihuana available in this country, one wonders how wise it is to introduce yet another potential hallucinogenic drug into our society. On the other hand, the sanctions for possession of marihuana are justified on lurid grounds and have created a genuine credibility gap which requires review.

There are obviously segments of our population—segments which cannot be identified entirely in advance—for whom the control of intake of marihuana would be wise. This drug, like LSD, does represent a lure away from the acquisition of competence even though a number of illicit users can control their intake without apparent social harm. In view of the evidence we can so readily see of poor judgment in the use of alcohol, of potent and high-risk drugs such as LSD, our society may not wish to encourage indiscriminate drug-taking and a pattern of free experimentation with any drug which alters consciousness. It may decide that, although some drug users manage without harm to themselves or to others, most tend to form themselves into cults of drug-takers who popularize, advertise, and expose the gullible amongst us to more than we can all comfortably or properly manage. If this is the case, some controls can be expected.

Yet, it is hard to see what can be gained by rash proposals for severe sanctions for the possession of LSD, barbiturates, and amphetamines. Some medical education and counteradvertising is indeed required to stop the contagion of drug use. We should be quite certain that such education and punishment of illicit traffic have truly failed before we create a new class of criminals.

Perhaps the Drug Abuse laws of 1965 are working. Indeed, since it is true that incitement to foolishness by the media has been truly consequential in the current contagion of drug use, one wonders why the advertising of LSD through a lurid press has not equally been considered a misdemeanor or a felony. I gather we would here encounter the first amendment!

We have arrived at a point where it may be possible for educated legislators, police, teachers, medical and research people, parole, judicial and law enforcement agencies to begin a collaboration in a sensible approach to the management and control of drug abuse. Our governments have tended to isolate agencies for drug-abuse control from those various communities which should be involved. We now must all exchange facts, call upon a range of experts to help to shape our society into one which uses whatever drugs it must with discrimination.

CHAPTER FOURTEEN

Youth and Family

Arthur Mandelbaum,*
Chief Psychiatric Social Worker,
The Menninger Foundation.

". . . a family lasts, for a while: the children are held to a magnetic center; then in time, the magnetism weakens, both of itself and its tiredness of aging and sorrow, and against the strength of the growth of each child, and against the strength of pulls from the outside, and one by one the children are drawn away." [1]

Just a few days ago, a mother said to me in the presence of her husband and their two adolescent children, "Why is it that raising a family is so difficult and complex now and frightens us so much?"

Her words of despair are echoed in the troubled feelings of many families these days. We are all somewhat frightened and bewildered by the swift changes we see; the music and movies produced by and for young people, their long hair, drugs, sex, their rebelliousness on the campus, their challenge to our values, their seeming disregard of the family and its traditions, and underneath it all, their struggles to liberate themselves.

---

[1]James Agee, "Let Us Now Praise Famous Men."

*Reprinted with permission from The Menninger Quarterly, Winter 1969-70.

By and large, adults do not like to remember their own adolescence, its storm and stress, its sorrows, and even its delights which may be tinged with feelings of shame and guilt. This is but one of the reasons for adults not understanding their children. Perhaps this is why we call it the generation gap.

The family consists of guiding forces—the mother and the father. They give a child some roots in the past, a sense of continuity, and a sense of belonging. They offer him guidelines which he can follow through the challenges of life experiences. When parents are consistently present for their child, are alert and responsive to his needs, and include him in the circle of family activity, the child absorbs into himself an image of his mother—and soon an image of his father—that become deeply etched into his personality. The transition from one developmental period to another during the early years is smoothed by consistent, available parents who create a sense of outer continuity, predictability and harmony that form a sense of inner security for the child. This is essential for giving a child an identity and sense of inner goodness and basic trust.

Some of our great authors understood this even before psychology became a science. In the novel, *Brothers Karamazov,* Dostoevski spoke of the profound meaning and importance of security in early life. "You must know there is nothing higher and stronger, more wholesome and good for life than some good memory, especially a memory of childhood. People talk to you a great deal about your education, but some good sacred memory preserved from childhood is perhaps the best education. If a man carries many such memories with him into life, he is sage to the end of his days. And if one has only one good memory left in one's heart, even that may sometimes be the means of saving him."

If a child has a good sense of basic trust, a sense of inner harmony and a grasp of who he is, he can glide a little more smoothly into young adulthood and perhaps parents can let go more easily too. But many parents and children cannot let go of each other. Thus, they place each other in a double bind saying grow, but hold tight; saying grow, but do not leave because we have little else; saying do your own thing, but not if it's different or new.

If parents resist emancipation strivings, adolescents then seek more rebellious ways to achieve independence. From the parental point of view, separation is a dangerous risk in a world which seems untrustworthy and irrational. Some parents are uneasy about the worth and quality of their own lives; they suffer life rather than seek to master and change it. When children watch parents take pills to master anxieties; when they watch them eat too much, drink too much, and accumulate too much, they begin to question the quality of their own lives. They turn to their peers who have the same doubts, and challenge the quality of the adult world and the style of life in it. Many parents worry over the loss of love from their children because they fail to see that their youngster is dissolving childish ties and childish dependence rather than renouncing and abandoning his parents.

In 1922, Ernest Jones spoke of adolescence as a recapitulation.

> The individual recapitulates and expands in the second decennium of life the development he passed through during the first five years. . . . Adolescence recapitulates infancy and . . . the precise way in which a given person will pass through the necessary stages of development in adolescence is to a very great extent determined by the form of his infantile development.

The attitudes and feelings of parents toward the child during the first five years of his life often seem recapitulated during the teen-age years. If parents were perplexed and bewildered during the child's early years, and unable to give him consistency and continuity, the child may find adolescence overwhelming and frightening. If the parents were concerned and frightened over separations, they will resist the adolescent's efforts to emancipate himself. If the parents feared the child's aggression and sexual strivings and refused to let him identify with them, adolescence will be viewed with repugnance. On the other hand, if the child's first years were calm and consistent, and development moved fairly smoothly from one stage to the next without unusual incident, the parents will likely have the strength, flexibility and tolerance for the unpredictable shifts which occur during adolescence.

When the adolescent comes for professional help, how and to what extent the parents are involved with his problems, and how much they should be involved with his treatment, can only be determined in a series of diagnostic interviews. There are times, albeit infrequently, when the adolescent applies for help on his own, calling his need to the attention of the school counselor, the family physician, the juvenile court officer or other important adults in his life. Nevertheless, it is essential to involve the parents.

> The timing of the decision as to when and how to bring the parents in is delicate, and it is a great temptation to overlook or greatly delay getting in touch with the parents when the adolescent is strongly upset and hostile toward them. It is dangerous to go far in the treatment of minors without parental consent, especially as the severity of the disturbance is difficult to evaluate. Gentle firmness of this point is usually acceded to by the young person.[2]

Many cases flounder because the preparation for treatment did not include the parents. If the parents are not involved in the outpatient treatment process, knowledge of the youngster's improvement can only come from the clinical process itself. What the child does on the outside, and what he does in relationship to his parents can only be guessed.

Some parents cannot see how demanding they are of their own children and how much they expect of them. Some cannot help their child renunciate infantile pleasures. These parents protect their own infantile longings, and are frightened of adult tasks: the requirements of being a mother and father and assisting the child to gradually yield his instinctual pleasures. They resent such parental responsibility and regard each developmental phase of the child's growth, and not adolescence alone, as arduous and a bitter struggle.

The adolescent's attempt at separation and emancipation will start reverberations which may go back to the first years of life. The history may reveal doubts and fears in the mother when the child began to walk away from her, separation difficulties when nursery school was attempted, a rocky transition from elemen-

---

[2]Garden Hamilton, *Psychotherapy in Child Guidance.*

tary school to junior high, from junior high school to high school. For the parents of all children, these normally are stress periods but for the parents of the troubled child they are unusually so. The parents will express themes of fear of separation, fear of losing the child, fear of their becoming not needed by the child, and fear of growing old. The child's growth into young adulthood is viewed as all loss, with little gratification for them. There is a lack of confidence that they have given anything worthwhile to the child, that he has internalized nothing of them, and therefore, with his new freedom he will do nothing well and will get into serious difficulties. Parents must have other emotional and social resources and interests besides a deep investment in their child. The child should not be the exclusive center of parents' lives.

There are powerful external forces also which cause family breakdowns, such as war, poverty, the trauma of slavery, the swiftness of technological changes. Under such conditions, the fabric of family life is torn and families become uncertain and feel a creeping sense of depersonalization. Children who suffer the impact of these disruptions and discontinuities may fail to become individualized and emancipated from their parents. They may cling to infantile pleasures and reject growth or make believe they find it through such pseudo devices as drugs or sexual license, giving them at least a temporary sense of freedom from the intense anxiety they sense in the world. The great mathmetician, Haldane, stated that he had tried morphine, heroin, marihuana and other varieties of drugs, but the alterations of consciousness due to these drugs were a poor disappointment compared to the excitement and stimulation and alterations of consciousness he found by his work. But the adolescent may find work harsh and intolerable and retreat from it because it means a distasteful adult world. Or he may seek revolution, and a destruction of old forms and of history he never understood and mastered.

Still other adolescents, and a great many of them, seek their own authentic voice and lives without destroying the world. They take history and sift out what is useful and discard the irrelevant and such young people give us new colorations, our new ideas, and become our new authentic voices within new societal forms. These become the creators of new laws, new systems and teach us new lessons from history.

But none of this is easy. If a family strives to give its children a true sense of freedom and liberation within a form which is coherent and is accompanied by a sense of trust and self-esteem, then that family has contributed its portion to taming the "savageness of man and making gentle the life of the world."

CHAPTER FIFTEEN

Youth and Drugs

Dr. Cecil Chamberlin,*
Staff Psychiatrist in the Children's Division
of The Menninger Foundation.

"I see no hope for the future of our people if they are dependent on the frivolous youth of today, for certainly all youth are reckless beyond words. When I was a boy, we were taught to be discreet and respectful of elders, but the present youth are exceedingly wise and impatient of restraint." (Hesiod, 8th Century, B.C.)

This statement made by a man eight centuries before the birth of Christ, certainly helps put our current concerns about youth into a more reassuring perspective. The older generation has felt concern and perplexity about the younger generation for a few thousand years. The generation gap is nothing new.

Although the phenomenon may not have changed much, our ability to understand and make sense of it has. With the aid of sciences such as psychology, psychiatry and sociology, we now know a good deal about why youth behave as they do and what to do to help them behave differently. We know that much of what the young person is like and what he does comes from his

*Reprinted from *The Menninger Quarterly*, Winter 1969-70. Copyright The Menninger Foundation 1970.

past life experiences and his basic and original biological endowment. Youth or adolescence is not a separate entity—there is no real gap between the generations. The generations exist in continuum, related intimately to what has gone before and to what will follow in later life. The cycle is part of the sea of life through which the human ship must sail. The way a child is reared, the presence or absence of loving care, discipline, training, parental attitudes and values, all lay the basic foundation on which the young person rests. Deviations from the norm, or unusual stresses during the pre-adolescent years, will result in difficult times later.

Generally the child's development comes to an end with the physical changes of puberty. The adolescent experiences increased aggressive and sexual urges, and at the same time, his own controls are weakened, making him more prone to behavioral expressions of these inner tensions. Adolescence usually is a time to be action-oriented, to do things, and to rebel. The adolescent experiences much psychological upset and turmoil out of which he must reintegrate an adult personality. This inner turmoil accounts for much of the moodiness, unpredictability and childishness that baffle many adults, and gives us the impression of utter chaos and disorder.

A young person has several important developmental tasks to accomplish in the few short years before becoming an adult. One job is to develop new and different ways of coping with his inner tensions. Another is to sever the child-like, dependent ties to his parents. The previously pleasant, relatively cooperative child now begins to question his parents' authority, to disagree with their viewpoints and oppose their wishes. This is a necessary part of healthy growth, but a very difficult phase, especially for the parents. As the young person disrupts his ties to his parents, he turns more to his own age group and adopts their ways and values, especially those that are different from adults. Long hair on boys, unusual dress, and language with special slang words and gestures all are examples of such different values.

As part of this separation-from-the-parents-process, the adolescent vacillates as he does in most other things, from a kind of preposterous pseudo-maturity to a child-like dependence. His child-like wish to be taken care of, as he was in early years, is at times rather strong, although he usually has to repudiate it and complain that adults won't let him go, or won't let him do this or that as he wishes to do.

A later task of the adolescent is that of finding an identity. He must make a vocational choice and establish a more firm and stable sense of who he is and where he is going in life.

Based on our current knowledge about youth and their families, we can understand much of the current problematic behavior that they present to us. Much of the problem can be related to struggles within the family, since adolescents' behavior is often designed to affect and disturb their parents. The parents, on the other hand, may be greatly upset because their children are not as they want them to be; the children may give expression to feelings that they, the parents, wish they could, but cannot allow themselves the freedom to carry out.

Delinquent behavior results from many factors, and certainly no one approach can explain it. Such behavior, however, is evidence of the young person's attempts to find solutions to and relief from tensions, both within himself, and between himself and others around him, often his family. Minor delinquent behavior may represent the struggle for independence and emancipation, while repeated and more serious offenses almost always signal the disturbed teen-ager.

The increasingly popular use of marihuana, LSD and related drugs may represent to youth other ways to be antiadult and antiestablishment, or again may be an attempt to establish a new and independent identity. Many young people see these drugs as their property and not belonging to the adult, law-abiding world. To most of them, the use of drugs does not represent a problem or misbehavior. The rather severely punitive laws relating to drug control reinforces this attitude and increases the interest in using them for some young people. It is a common bond of youth to do the forbidden act together, a form of silent protest. One junior high school boy said, "There's one thing I can really scare my parents with—that is to tell them about the dope I take."

Youth are extremely effective in keeping knowledge of this drug-taking within their youth group. It is a widespread phenomenon in many communities, including this one, that we adults and parents know little about. It is their world and not many of us are in on it. What was once a ripple of drug interest has now become a tidal wave, sweeping over the country and the young people as though there were no obstacles in its path. "In this drug revolution, we adults are the least informed," said Dr. Joseph Downing, a psychiatrist who works with young people in California. Young people know about drugs from taking them, talking about them, and reading the scientific and popular literature about them. Many of them also know that their interest in drugs represents only one of many things that concerns them in today's world. Of most concern to them, and hopefully to us, is the widening gap between the generations; a gap that exists because of young people's values based upon present experiences and adults' established values based upon past experiences.

Drug use may also represent a search for relief from tensions of adolescent turmoil. One high school girl often took a stimulant, more commonly called "speed," when she became depressed over troubles with her boy friend or arguments with her parents in order to create a more pleasant experience with herself by counteracting the depression. A 16-year-old boy took LSD whenever he experienced any strong, unpleasant emotions because he thought he found his feelings were dulled, and therefore hurt less for several days after using the drug. Many young people picked up for drug use come from broken homes and serious family conflict. Others, who may be better adjusted and who may not be picked up often, come from homes in which there is a great deal of emphasis placed on achievement, competition and conformity. Many young people use drugs, especially marihuana, for its anxiety-relieving effect, and often mirror the example set by parents who take sedatives and tranquilizers.

The use of drugs may represent a temporary trial—while looking for new and exciting experiences—as the adolescent explores his ever-expanding world. A ninth-grade student at a local junior high school eagerly smoked marihuana for the first time when it was offered him by some high school students because he saw it as a way of doing what the older and very much admired group did—a way of growing up. "My friends told me a lot about all the pretty colors and things they saw when they took acid, so I just wanted to try it and see for myself—wow!"

The trial may be brief for many of these young people, and then they are through with drugs. For others, drug use may be prolonged. Those who do go further with drugs often are lonely, unhappy people who are desperately trying to establish some form of psychological balance. Unfortunately, our world today has little stability to offer them as they search for a port in the storm. For many, the very prohibition challenges youth to try drugs. For others, such chemicals seem to offer the hope of finding new solutions to the age-old problems of youth. A high school boy felt he could gain a better understanding of himself or his problems by using the so-called mind-expanding drugs, so he began taking them, hoping to find the answers.

Some people think that the present generation has turned away from the inner spiritual experience. Our society and much of our religion has become externally directed and socially oriented, neglecting the extremely important inner spiritual experience. Dr. Downing states, "As teen-agers say, we have put down our feelings and turned off. But the spiritual need is still there, all the stronger because our family ties often are bent if not broken, our values materialistic rather than personal. Many fathers spend their lives in the office or on the golf course, rather than with their children. Many parents have values of social prestige and high grades, rather than beauty and laughter. As our standards of living have gone up, our standards of loving have gone down."

As well as being concerned about young people who use drugs, we also should become concerned about ourselves and our lack of willingness to try to reach across the generation gap. We need to look at the examples we are setting for our young, at the distance between us and young people, at our refusal to accept the truth about ourselves and our society. Young people are looking, and they are using some of the drugs in the hope of seeing more clearly.

For some, the problems related to drug usage are far more serious than the examples I have given. One very depressed boy told me he wanted to take an overdose to blow his mind permanently, meaning to lose contact with reality so that he would be unable to re-establish it. This was his solution to overwhelming problems within himself and within his family.

These are some views about the current problems of youth. As you see, they contain no answers. The solutions must be found by youth and adults working together. Here at The Menninger Foundation, we are searching for some of the answers in our own Carriage House Project.

The Carriage House was established by volunteer staff members as a meeting place for teen-agers and young adults with problems. Young people hold informal discussions there, talking about such things as dropping out of school, problems with parents, and drug use. We hope that this new project will provide an acceptable setting for youth who feel alienated from traditional helping agencies such as the courts, schools and counseling centers.

Some additional remarks by Dr. Downing point to some of the ways to solve the current problems: "I suggest that one way to begin is to put aside our robe of adult omniscience and ask the young people what their experiences are; what they think can be done. I further suggest we attempt to find out what is happening in the teen-age culture. For example, we could listen to our teen-agers' records, what the singers are saying and what the teen-agers are hearing from Dylan, Donovan, and Simon and Garfunkel. We could send an expeditionary force, suitably disguised, to the teen-age dance halls. We might go so far as to invite some teen-age LSD users to talk with us informally. We need to make two-way contact with this age group: the adjusted young people who have the same standards as ourselves, and also with the drug users, the juvenile offenders, the runaways and the dropouts. By listening, by trying to understand, by showing that we care what they do and by not condemning them, we can make contact. If we make contact and maintain it, then we have a chance to bring them to realization of their social opportunities and obligations, but if we don't, we can't force them. Like it or not, we must respect their decision to be different; at the same time we expect them to respect our way of life and our differences."

The most articulate message that comes from youth is their music, and we need to listen. The more we turn it off because it is too loud, the more we are missing what they are trying to say to us. The more we refuse to listen, the louder the music may become. Listen to these lyrics which convey youth's point of view:

> As time begins to burn itself upon me
> And the days are growing short
> People try their hardest to reject me
> In a way their conscience won't be caught
> Something is happening to me day by day
> My pebble on the beach is getting washed away
> I've given everything that was mine to give
> And now I'll turn around and find that there's
> No time to live.

> So after I have seen the wheel of fortune
> Spinning for the man who holds the ace
> There's many who would change
> Their places for him
> But none of them have seen his lonely face
> Something is happening to me day by day
> My pebble on the beach is getting washed away
> I've given everything that was mine to give
> And now I'll turn around and find that there's
> No time to live.*

Of course youth has its problems, some very serious, and the manifestations of these problems affect us all. Youth repudiates our values, they point out our failures, and their idealism distresses us. But in all this lies hope for a change for the better, for progress in the future.

I agree with these lines from "Always the Young Strangers," by Carl Sandburg: "One thing I know deep out of my time: Youth, when lighted and alive and given a sporting chance, is strong for struggle and not afraid of any toils or punishments or dangers or deaths. What shall be the course of society and civilization across the next hundred years? For the answers, read if you can the strange and baffling eyes of youth. Yes, for the answers read if you can the strange and baffling eyes of youth."

---

*"No Time to Live" by Steve Winwood and Jim Capaldi (Traffic).

CHAPTER SIXTEEN

If Your Child Takes Drugs . . .

Dr. Richard H. Blum,* of Stanford University,
is a pioneer in the study of what attracts young people
to drugs and motivates others to react against them.
He sets forth his views on the relations beween
parent and child in the following interview.

What advice would you give to parents who are reasonably certain that their children have begun to do some experimenting with illegal drugs?

Well, my first question to the parents is: Why are they only "reasonably certain?" Why don't they ask the child? And if they already have a family situation where the children are behaving secretively, they probably have a bit of conventional mystery behavior, which all children love. This is sexual exploration when they are aged five, or smoking Hollyhock stems when they are eight, or maybe smoking pot when they are fifteen, and one should expect from them these minor secret societies. I think we can know pretty well whether the dalliance with mystery is simply on the level with playtime and fantasy. The more serious problem is regular use of *any*

*Dr. Blum is project director for psychopharmacology at The Institute for the Study of Human Problems, Stanford University. He has served on the President's Commission on Law Enforcement and the Administration of Justice. He is the author of a number of books, including *The Utopiates: The Use and Users of LSD-25; Alcoholism: Modern Phychological Approaches to Treatment;* and, with others, *Drugs and Society and Students and Drugs.*

illicit substance, and I mean tobacco and alcohol, as well as non-prescription amphetamines and marihuana. Our concern then is *how* do we talk to children about being lawful or healthy in regard to the use of available but dangerous materials? "Dangerous" here assumes that when people are growing up the last thing they need are some chemicals that nature did not decide to put inside. (The exceptions would be undernourished children who need vitamins, but in normal nourishment I presume nature is smarter than we are, and I think most physicians in the business of healing would agree that the most we can do is help.)

In any event, my own philosophy, and I simply offer this as a personal belief, is that communication to children about "no no's" should begin very early, indeed, and not necessarily on a rational or reasonable level. Three-year-olds don't need a long discussion of the pharmacology of aspirin. All they need to be told, in totally certain terms, is that everything in that medicine chest is out of reach. You have to teach emotionally about things that are important, and we are in the midst of a family study right now where we are comparing the children of families where the kids have gotten in drug troubles with families whose children have not. These are middle-class families, controlled for economic circumstances, and so forth, and we find a great reluctance in them to take responsibility for providing structure for the kids. I don't mean to sound here like something out of the medieval woods, and it is curious that I feel I have to say that. Any effort on our part to create direction or controls makes us feel bad. It is curious; it is deadly wrong.

I think America has always had trouble handling authority. We have mothers in our family study who will say to their children, when we discussed it with them, "Well, the child has to make up his own mind whether he is going to take LSD or not . . . he is going to be seven . . . well, yes, we have to give responsibility at an early age." What they mean is that *they* have to shirk it at an early age, and to give the seven-year old the responsibility for making up his mind whether or not to take LSD, or whether or not to drive the family car, or whether or not to take the family .45 out of the chest, in which it should not be, and blaze away. I am using extreme notions but this is what we see.

One of our psychoanalytic colleagues is doing a study in San

Francisco for us and making some observations on the fantasies of parents who cannot act like parents. There is a historical tragedy with them because their parents could not act like parents either, so we have a nation of people without models themselves on how instinctively to act in firm and loving ways simultaneously.

We also have the fantasy of parents as children, so the democratic or really egalitarian family where nobody takes responsibility is a family which is, if you will, overly dedicated to youthfulness. And so the forty-year-old parents think they are twelve also, or five, at an unconscious level. We have made such a cult of youth that we have dived down to the ten-year-old level. I think we probably are in trouble as a consequence, and not out of any evil intent but just out of the accident, whatever social accident it was, that led us to want to be loved without being willing to be disliked by our children when we prevented them from doing things that were dangerous.

A parent should not be in a popularity contest with his child. He cannot be seeking and currying the favor of the child and living in constant fear that one day the child is going to say a bad word to him. The problem of child-raising is the problem of putting an immense amount of energy in, an immense amount of energy—it is astonishing—to make something grow, to give it direction. It is not just love, it is thoughtfulness, form and a direction. If the parents do not transmit it, the child will get it, but he will get it from his peers.

One of the things that seems so difficult for families these days is that the peer group has taken on immense importance. For example, just after the war there were some studies done at Harvard on cigarette smoking which show that one of the things that attracted most of the adolescent smoking behavior was the smoking behavior of parents.

However, a study last year by the American Cancer Society showed that the most important single influence on them now was the behavoir of their peers. We see, I think, the same thing in our study of marihuana and alcohol. The parents really do not matter as much as they used to. Peers matter a lot. We have, in a sense, created a generation gap by idealizing age group cohorts. This is a crazy way of saying, "All of us who are three-year-olds got to stick together against them four-year-olds." We have created a consciousness of age as a binder for a group, and of course we do it not just by the fact that we put kids together in age groups in school and the kids naturally stay together in age groups because of common interests. (Although I must say that this is different from the old days in a farm family where kids were always exposed to other ages.) We have also advertised for it: The "Pepsi Generation," after all, inculcates this insulation. In so far as we provide stratified little societies for twelve-year-olds, thirteen-year-olds, fourteen-year-olds, we have created a series of cross-sectional segments in our society, each of which joins to reject those older (they don't take much interest in those younger). And that is a hazard for parents. You may say, "Well, you can change all that." I haven't the foggiest idea how.

What would you say to parents who complain about not knowing how to talk to their children about drug use?

When you talk about being a parent you start when the child begins. If you follow the rule of talking for fifteen years, and being a responsible parent for fifteen years, and knowing your child fairly well, and not showing blindness to his obvious anxieties or defects, as they may be, and thereby not making him cruelly carry the burden himself; but rather, if it is a family where everybody knows each other very well and talks to each other, you anticipate in advance the risks. So, we talk to children now and train them about automobiles, and we may even warn them about child molesters. We tell them that they are going to have to go to school, and we prepare them for that, if we are middle-class. Nowadays, parents also have to prepare children to enter a drug-permeated atmosphere with the knowledge that by the time the kid is in the sixth grade in an urban area he is going to be exposed to most things, and by the time he is in the eighth grade: everything. And they have to talk about it to the kids reasonably. I think if they have not done that, then of course it is the usual problem of an after the fact—"now what do we do?"

I can only say this: That most kids get through it anyway, and survive, and if they are just smoking a little pot, well there are lot more important things in the world to worry about than that. Even if they have used LSD once or twice, which I would prefer they would not, for their own sakes, if that is all they have done and intend to quit on their own, as most do, you might say, "Well, my dear friend, I am glad you have survived this extra hazard of our technological society: congratulations."

Now, in point of fact, we are going to get an increasing number of kids who are in trouble. The numbers of collegians playing with heroin are small, but the numbers of high school kids taking barbiturates or heroin are considerable, and those kids, again, need to be told beforehand that the world is full of dangerous chemicals.

What about the parents who have not been aware of drugs until, for example, their nineteen-year old child becomes a member of a commune which is taking drugs?

I don't believe it. No, I believe there are such parents, but I don't believe that they had no idea that their child was suddenly going to run away from home and join a commune. I cannot imagine that they lived twenty-four hours together in a family for nineteen years and had not noticed something about who the child was with, and what his values were, and how he felt about things, and what dissatisfactions he had. They really would have had to have had that child locked in a cell for nineteen years, or themselves, not to have had any inkling until he suddenly ran away. And we have to, I think, coldly and cruelly get rid of the, well really, the self-esteem and self-protecting lies which we tell ourselves.

With the child in crisis, or the parent in crisis, the easiest answer is that, if they are still there at all, for goodness' sake start talking right away and in a hurry. We are talking about communication after there has been a nineteen-year hiatus and you can expect some considerable differences of views and a very painful period. But if you are really interested in communication you are just going to have to put up with it, or return to where you were before, and stop talking again. This is unnecessary and tragic, which is not to assume that anybody in this case is wrong or to be blamed. Most humans do the things they do by accident and most things are beyond their control, I believe. I do not think that most kids are that different from their parents after all. If the parent focuses on the superficial differences—long hair and the antagonistic, provocative statements, and fails to note that this child, like him, has blue eyes, brown hair, pale complexion, speaks English, wears shoes, knows how to use a knife and fork, and all of the basic forms of behavior which are already inculcated, then he will not see that their area of difference is really relatively small.

What would you have to say to parents who realized that their children were going to meet drugs in the schools?

Again, I think we have to handle drugs as we handle guns, knives and automobiles, ever present tools in the environment with no more and no less mention than that. The problem is not so much informing them about drugs, which does not take too long providing we have basic knowledge of each of the substances. The problem is what the taking of drugs *means* to the kids, and I think we have to talk about preparing children to resist influences of peers. The family might say, "Now, we know that you are going to City High School, and we know that the opportunity in that City High School is to do one of a hundred things because there are a hundred groups. You may, if you want, become a prostitute working for one of the high school pimps. You may, if you want, become valedictorian in a group of intellectuals, you may join an athletic team, you may be fascinated by the drop-out crowd, you may become very interested in one of the church-related groups. All of these opportunities exist and I think all of them have to be reviewed." And when the kid perks up his eyes and ears about one or two of them and says, "That might interest me," then you had better explore where it would lead him, whether it is the church, or the valedictorian, or the drug crowd.

And we are not talking just about high school, we are talking about junior high; even now in California in the fourth grade. So we might say, "Look, the facts of drugs are very simple. Most drugs are probably not to be used except in some kind of socially-sanctioned situation." For a social drug like alcohol, this means probably learning how to drink wine at home at the table; not to learn to take spirits at the corner for the first time, which is a pattern associated with high risk of alcoholism.

With home drugs we teach the same thing. We should not say, "Tomorrow you are going into the sixth grade and I know there is marihuana in that new school, and I don't want you to touch any because drugs are bad" and, at the same time, when the child is sleepless, give him a tranquilizer which has not been prescribed for him. Our actions have to match our words throughout, and I think the task is to say, "Well, now what would it mean in this high school? What do these kids look like to you who are simply experimenting with marihuana?" If the kid says, "Well, everybody does," and the parent says, "Well, does that include you?," and the kid says, "Well, I guess it has to include me if all my friends are doing it." Well, that is a very good point to start a conversation, not because you are concerned about the child taking half a joint of marihuana once in his life, or three times, or so on. But if he has to do what his friends are doing, then we have to be very concerned about him, not because of drugs, but because he is not yet a person strong enough to go into the world, carrying the family values. At the first joust the other knight will unseat him and the family values. What we know from our own research to date is that families who are most successful know what their values are, tell the kids that what the family believes in is really important, reinforce the kids in their actual behavior, have the whole family do it together, and in fact provide the child with an awful lot of support and gratification within the family structure. And if the family provides the gratification and if the kid looks, and knows that the family is important and exists, then peers are secondary and can stay that way. This does not mean that the kid does not "get along" or does not enjoy his classmates. It means that when they all decide to drive 90 miles an hour, dead drunk down the turnpike, he has the strength enough to say, "No, I think not, friends, I think I will go home and go to sleep."

If the problem is an overresponsiveness on the part of the child to leaders, then we must address ourselves to the quality of leaders he is seeking, and pay some attention to the group he is in. If he is choosing a group of "baddies" then we have to wonder what there is in our child that makes the baddies so attractive.

What kind of things in the child would make the baddies so attractive?

The parents' delinquency, for one thing. We are kind of a lawless society. And we are also, as human beings, I suspect, all pretty savage at heart. We have great potentials for almost everything: Dachau; the Mongol Invasions of Russia; the destruction of the American Indian; the Mona Lisa; beautiful buildings; but none of this happened accidentally.

The potentials within parents are the same, and if the parents are sitting on top of a bunch of hostile or delinquent impulses which, when expressed by a child, bring a secret gladness to the tiny, hidden, dark heart of the parent, that is one reason why they occur. If you watch, for example, the shouts and roars of some of my faculty colleagues, of glee and delight when a couple of hundred radical students burn down the president's office, or dump red paint on the president at my august university, which is Stanford, and see the enthusiasm with which the faculty may greet the delinquency of the youngsters, usually directed against authority, I don't need to ask very hard about where one strong source of support came for juvenile delinquency. Similarly, we, as parents, have to make sure that what our children are doing is not something we secretly admire or secretly wanted to have done ourselves. It is well to begin examining our childrens' behavior by looking inside ourselves. Our children began there and may still be there in some ways.

We also know that lawlessness, as such, is increasingly attractive in our society. It is very easy and kind of fun to destroy. We do know that all of us kind of hate discipline and it is therefore not so surprising that people destroy, and break laws and go to war. What is surprising is that civilization has worked at all to keep them from doing that. And if, as we watch our children choosing the "baddies," while this may be socially abnormal in a civilized neighborhood, it is not biologically abnormal. We may look at it as unfortunate, and again the usual devices for control are to discuss, to command, to reward for good behavior, to punish for bad. I don't think that any of the parents I know are surprised to hear this. But I think if we look at the parents we know, we might be surprised to see how few do use the tools at their command.

Do you have anything to say to the young users who may find themselves drawn to drugs and who may blame their parents for its attraction?

Well, I think we all, watching ourselves, know that nothing but the noblest reasons account for anything that any of us do, and so I am sure that, if we asked our young as well as our older friends why they are doing what they are, they will find a whole set of absolutely virtuous statements by which to record the history and outcome of their current conduct. And when challenged we also know that blame-throwing is certainly what people learn to throw first, and it does keep us from being uncomfortable. So it is that if people do things which make them feel bad, they tend not to admit that they are at fault and they may tend not to admit that they are feeling bad, and so obviously they blame others.

It is wonderful for kids to blame parents, it is perhaps one of the most common popular sports; I think it probably exceeds baseball and football in popularity, and there is no entrance fee. Parents can be shot at for free. So, the function of children's blaming is "they are bad and I am good and I wish they hadn't called it to my attention that I am feeling so bad about what I am doing if I am really in a delinquent crowd." And, of course, it is important to keep calling it to their attention because if they are in a delinquent crowd, we want to get them out.

The reasons for adolescent misbehavior are legion. The terribly important thing is for the parents not to believe their children when the children blame the parents. The parents probably did not plan for the children to come out that way, and if the children blame the parents' misdeeds for bringing them there, it also assumes too much knowledge on the children's part and how they got to where they were. As humans we like to assign causes but we rarely know. The parents may feel, I think, a righteous indignity when so accused, which does not mean that they should not examine their hearts to see if indeed it may not be correct. There may very well be things that parents do that are absolutely ridiculous and painful to children, and do drive children into spasms.

Do you think that any of the drug education programs that are currently being launched under federal sponsorship will prove effective?

Well, America has always placed a great burden on education. We demand a lot of formal education, and have had great success really in using it as the primary tool for moulding a society. The melting pot was on the stove in a school room; it was in school rooms that children of immigrants learned the same language and the same values, and it was to school rooms that their parents went for adult education to learn a common culture. In the controversy now about schools and integration, we have put the greatest burden for America again onto schools—thus, the bussing, which is grotesquely difficult for everybody. But, somehow, we believe that the school will do it where everybody has failed.

I think we are asking the same of the school in the drug area. The business of rationality is a western dream, and a lovely one. The Greeks really gave us a great deal including a crude possibility—a myth that we are a rational people. And out of that myth we have created a great educational system. And we were right enough, often enough, to have developed a very interesting semirational society. We do know how to make automobiles; we have more trouble making marriages. We do make factories; we have more trouble making treaties with foreign powers that stick. If we look where schools have succeeded, it is primarily in vocational training and in the melting pot of people with common aspirations for wealth, status and a sense of community.

I am not sure that in the drug field the schools are going to be able to make it because we have not noticed that the schools are a proper force for the transmission of moral values. The schools teach technology and vocations very well because these are not moral educations.

When we are talking about education for drugs we are talking about education in the fourth, fifth, sixth, seventh and eighth grades. It has to be done there; that is where their exposure to drugs is. So you have to start in kindergarten, and you say, "Well, is rationality about the use of pharmaceutical preparations going to be transmitted at that level?" We do pretty well in the schools teaching traffic safety, I guess, about driving, even for kids walking—maybe we will manage it. But I would like to suggest that, at the moment, our educational endeavors are a great delusion. Right now we are mixing morality and outright fantasy about drugs.

Can you cite any programs that have been successful in teaching students about drugs?

I would love to be able to say, "I know seven school systems that have conducted controlled experiments in teaching where they learned where the kids are; what the kids expect and think and are doing; what stage they are in; and about their peer pressures. They then give fifteen kinds of teaching programs, each to match samples of kids. And then they have looked, over the past three years, to see how these children differ in outcome with regard to their drug use, which is the essence of a controlled follow-up study."

In fact, I don't know of a single study in the United States which even evaluates any drug education that has ever been done. I don't know of a study where they have even tested the kids after they have given them a drug education course to see if they were *awake*. If we look at the millions of dollars that we are spending on advertising now against cigarettes, we can say, "Well, we have noticed that cigarette consumption has dropped." So now that they are starting with TV and radio spots for other drugs, they can point to the cigarette business and say, "Well, maybe it will work." Cancer is a very strong argument, and gets through, I think, although it took twenty years even to persuade people to accept that argument. But the arguments about marihuana are much less persuasive than cancer.

What is your response to the argument of some young users that drug-taking is a purely private matter?

The question is—just very selfishly—"Does it damage the community in which I live, does it raise my taxes because I have to take care of them in a hospital?"

Does it?

Sure it does. But then I don't mind paying taxes to pay for people's health care generally. No objection whatsoever. I would like, however, to control the use of substances or materials that are most likely to produce damaging effects and for which I cannot anticipate many benefits.

The problem of "what is private" is quite curious in terms of "Is your body your own?" And, of course, it is not. If you think about how society dresses it, society decides. If you think whether you should walk in the middle of a crowded street or not, either the policeman or the automobile will decide that. If you get sick and fall down you will have to be picked up by somebody else. If, with that body, we take something that gives us riotous notions that we can drive drunk better than we can sober, and we kill somebody, it seems to me not a bit different.

Now the argument that "the drug is harmless and so consequently the body will not harm another," is fine. Then we simply have to be sure that either the drug is harmless, or more important, that the person who takes it will not harm another. And then we have to recognize that some people can take drugs quite safely, whether it is alcohol or cigarettes. Most people who take cigarettes do not die from cancer, if you want to look at it that way. Most people who drink do not become alcoholics. Most people who take LSD do not go to the hospital. I will not say that most people who take heroin do not become addicts. I am not sure.

I do not think people's bodies belong to them. If we look at ourselves as social animals, which we are, we need each other too much. And, consequently, what each of us does really does matter to the other person. If you hit me, whether you have a drug in you or not, is of no consequence to me; I still hurt. The concern, then, is with the behavior of persons, and then the argument gets to where I think it ought to be. What do people do and do drugs make any difference? For some people they do not, for a few people they do.

We, in America, I think, have a great hope that by passing a law we can change behavior. I am not nearly so optimistic. I am particularly pessimistic about changes in the criminal law as making a dent in the behavior of large numbers of our otherwise important young citizens. I personally favor the very considerable decriminalization of the codes with regard to all forms of drug use. I favor regulation, generally, but very little use of criminal law. Consequently, the omnibus drug bill, as it stands, still represents an attempt to apply the criminal law to the control, the shaping of human behavior, in an area that strikes me as clearly one where we have not been able to do that very successfully, looking at prohibition or what has happened to marihuana. I am very grateful for a reduction of penalties in the new law so that we may indeed have probation and so forth. My own bias is that, given regulation needs as I see them, the best we could have would be some kind of regulatory statute which controls the distribution on some substances, and which taxes users for insisting on risking themselves, if risks are there, to provide sufficient funds for hospitalization of any who end up sick. That is about it.

CHAPTER SEVENTEEN

Drug Use and Student Values

Kenneth Keniston,* Ph.D.,
Associate Professor of Psychiatry, School of Medicine,
Yale University, at a Drug Education Conference,
Washington, D.C.

In the comments to follow, I will argue that student drug use is closely related to pressures on American students, and is but a variant of values that are shared by many and perhaps most American undergraduates today. To be sure, only a small minority turn toward drugs; but the members of this minority group are but first cousins to the more normal college student. In particular, the student drug user shares with his non-drug-using classmates an active search for meaning through intense personal experience.

In order to understand the values shared by many American college students, we must begin by considering some of the pressures that affect today's students. With regard to drug use, two pressures are particularly important: the pressure toward cognitive professionalism, and the pressure toward psychological numbing.

Cognitive professionalism

The past two decades have seen a revolution in our expecta-

---

* Dr. Keniston is the author of two widely acclaimed books on youth, *The Uncommitted* and *Young Radicals: Notes on Committed Youth.*

tions about college students. Rising standards of academic performance in primary and secondary schools, the baby boom of the war, the slowness with which major American universities have expanded their size—all have resulted in increasing selectivity by the admissions offices of the most prestigious American colleges and universities. Furthermore, once a student is admitted to college, higher admission standards have meant that more could be demanded of him; students who a generation ago would have done A work now find themselves doing only C work with the same effort. The sheer volume of required reading and writing has increased enormously; in addition, the quality of work expected has grown by leaps and bounds. Finally, for a growing number of young Americans, college is but a stepping stone to professional and graduate school after college; and as a result, consistent academic performance in college increasingly becomes a prerequisite for admission to a desirable business school, medical school, law school or graduate school.

Not only have academic pressures mounted in the past generation, but these pressures have become more and more cognitive. What matters, increasingly, to admissions committees and college graders is the kind of highly intellectual, abstracting, reasoning ability that enables a student to do well on college boards, graduate records and other admission tests, and—once he is in college or graduate school—to turn out consistently high grades that will enable him to overcome the next academic hurdle. And while such intellectual and cognitive talents are highly rewarded, colleges increasingly frown upon emotional, nonintellectual and passionate forms of expression.

In contrast to these cognitive demands, there are extremely few countervailing pressures to become more feeling, morally responsible, courageous, artistically perceptive, emotionally balanced, or interpersonally subtle human beings. On the contrary, the most visible pressures on today's students are in many ways antiemotional, impersonal, quantitative and numerical.

Increasingly, then, one of the major pressures on American students is a pressure to perform well academically, to postpone and delay emotional satisfactions until they are older, to refine and sharpen continually their cognitive abilities. As a result, students today probably work harder than students in any other previous generation; a bad course or a bad year means to many of them that they will not get into graduate school. Taking a year off increasingly means running the danger of getting drafted and being sent to Vietnam.

Thus, while the systematic quest for cognitive competence occupies much of the time and effort of the preprofessional student at today's selective colleges, this pursuit does little to inform the student about life's wider purposes. One of the peculiar characteristics of professional competence is that even when competence is attained, all of the other really important questions remain unanswered: what life is all about, what really matters, what to stand for, how much to stand for, what is meaningful, relevant and important, what is meaningless, valueless and false. Thus, for many students, the pursuit of professional competence must be supplemented by another, more private and less academic quest for the meaning of life. Academic efforts seem, to a large number of students, divorced from the really important "existential" and "ultimate" questions. In this way, the student's private search for meaning, significance and relevance are experienced as unconnected with or opposed to his public exertions for grades, academic success and professional competence. How students search for significance and relevance of course varies enormously from individual to individual; but as I will later suggest, drug use seems—to a small group of students—a pathway to the pursuit of meaning.

Stimulus-flooding and psychological numbing

Every society contains pressures and demands which its members simply take for granted. Thus, the pressure for extremely high levels of cognitive efficiency seems to most of us a necessary and an even desirable aspect of modern society. Our response to the second social pressure I want to discuss is even more unreflective and automatic. This second pressure has to do with the sheer quantity, variety and intensity of external stimulations, imagery and excitation to which most Americans are subjected. For lack of a better label, I will term the condition one of increasing "stimulus-flooding."

Most individuals in most societies have at some point in their lives had the experience of being so overcome by external stimulation and internal feelings that they gradually find themselves growing numb and unfeeling. Medical students, for example, commonly report that after their first and often intense reactions to the cadaver in the dissecting room, they simply "stop feeling anything" with regard to the object of their dissection. Or we have all had the experience of listening to so much good music, seeing so many fine paintings, being so overwhelmed by excellent cooking that we find ourselves simply unable to respond further to new stimuli. Similarly, at moments of extreme psychic pain and anguish, most individuals "go numb," no longer perceiving the full implications of a catastrophic situation or no longer experiencing the full range of their own feelings.

This psychological numbing operates, I submit, at a great variety of levels for modern man. Our experience from childhood onward with the constantly flickering images and sounds of telesion, films, radio, newspapers, paperbacks, neon signs, advertisements and sound trucks, numbs us to many of the sights and sounds of our civilization. The exposure of the most intelligent men to a vast variety of ideologies, value systems, philosophies, political creeds, superstitions, religions and faiths numbs us, I think, to the unique claims to validity and the special spiritual and intellectual values of each one: we move among values and ideologies as in a two-dimensional landscape.

In all these respects, modern men confront the difficult problems of keeping stimulation from without to a manageable level, while at the same time protecting themselves against being overwhelmed by their own inner responses to the stimuli from the outer world. Defenses or barriers against both internal and external stimulation are, of course, essential in order for us to preserve our intactness and integrity as personalities. From earliest childhood, children develop thresholds of responsiveness and barriers against stimulation in order to protect themselves against being overwhelmed by inner or outer excitement. Similarly in adulthood, comparable barriers, thresholds and defenses are necessary, especially when we find ourselves in situations of intense stimulation.

Thus, in at least a minority of Americans, the normal capacity to defend oneself against undue stimulation and inner excitation is exaggerated and automatized, so that it not only protects but walls off the individual from inner and outer experience. In such individuals, there develops an acute sense of being trapped in their own shells, unable to break through their defenses to make contact with experience or with other people, a sense of being excessively armored, separated from their own activities as by an invisible screen, estranged from their own feelings and from potentially emotion-arousing experiences in the world. Presumably most of us have had some inkling of this feeling of inner deadness and outer flatness, especially in times of great fatigue, let-down, or depression. The world seems cold and two-dimensional; food and life have lost their savor; our activities are merely going through the motions, our experiences lack vividness, three-dimensionality and intensity. Above all, we feel trapped or shut in our own subjectivity.

Each of the two pressures I have discussed—cognitive professionalism and stimulus-flooding—evoke characteristic responses among today's American students. The pressure for cognitive professional competence leads to a search for meaning in other areas of life; the feeling and fear of psychological numbing leads to a pursuit, even a cult, of experiences for their own sake. And use and abuse of psychoactive drugs by students is closely related to these two themes in student values.

The search for meaning

Among today's self-conscious students, the statement, "I'm having an identity crisis" has become a kind of verbal badge of honor, a notch in the gun, a scalp at the belt. But although the term "identity crisis" can be easily parodied and misused, it points to fundamental issues of adolescence in all societies that are particularly heightened in our own society. Since academic pursuits, on the whole, tell the student so little about life's ultimate purposes, students are turned back upon their own resources to answer questions like, "What does life mean? What kind of person am I? Where am I going? Where do I come from? What really matters?"

To understand this search for meaning, we must recall that many of the traditional avenues to meaning and significance have dried up. Traditional religious faith is not, for most sophisticated undergraduates, a means of ascertaining the meaning of life: traditional religions often seem to students to be worn out, in-sincere, or superficial. Similarly, the great classic political ide-ologies, whether they be political liberalism, conservatism, marxism or fascism, arouse relatively little interest among most undergraduates. Nor does the "American Way of Life," as epit-omized by 100 % Americanism and free enterprise, stir most stu-dents to enthusiasm, much less provide them with answers about life's ultimate purposes.

One by one, then, many of the traditional sources of meaning have disappeared at the very same time that academic life itself, because of its intense pressure and professional specialization, seems to many students increasingly irrelevant to their major existential concerns. Where, then, do students turn?

The cult of experience

The cult of experience has often been discussed as a defining characteristic of American youth cultures. Central to this cult is a focus on the present—on today, on the here-and-now. Thus, rather than defer gratification and enjoyment for a distant future, immediate pleasure and satisfaction are emphasized. Rather than reverence for the traditions of the past, experience in the present is stressed. Psychologically, then, such human qualities as con-trol, planning, waiting, saving, and postponing on the one hand, and revering, recalling, remembering and respecting on the other, are equally deemphasized. In contrast, activity, adventure, re-sponsiveness, genuineness, spontaneity and sentience are the new experiential values. Since neither the future nor the past can be assumed to hold life's meaning, the meaning of life must be sought within present experience, within the self, within its ac-tivity and responsiveness in the here-and-now.

Disaffiliation and drugs

The two student values I have discussed—the search for mean-ing and the cult of experience—are intimately related to the pressures I have outlined earlier. The search for meaning is made more urgent by the amount of time and energy the average stu-dent must spend in preprofessional academic pursuits that often appear to him irrelevant to his basic concerns. And the cult of experience is intensified by the fear or feeling in many undergraduates that, instead of becoming more open to themselves and to experience, they are becoming increasingly numbed and closed off from all that is exciting and beautiful. Both of these values are, as well, related to the use and abuse of drugs by students. For such is the cultism and propaganda that surrounds drugs, especially the hallucinogens, that many students have come to feel that states induced by these drugs will automatically produce a revelation of life's meaning, or at least an experience which itself will be highly significant and illuminating. Similarly, to the undergraduate who feels himself unduly walled-off from experience, drugs like the hallucinogens and the amphetamines (which intensify and alter ordinary states of consciousness) may seem a chemical sledgehammer for breaking out of his shell.

Obviously, despite the congruence of drug use with important student values in American colleges, the vast majority of American students do not seek meaning and experience primarily via psychoactive compounds. Despite the presence of some values which are consistent with drug use, most students have other values that argue against drug use. It is only a minority who are persuaded to choose drugs as a primary means of searching for meaning.

I doubt that it is possible to present an exact portrait of the type of student who is likely to use and abuse drugs. My own experience with student drug-users convinces me that there are many different motives for drug use and abuse, and there are many different factors—psychological, sociological, cultural and situational—that determine whether one student will use drugs while another will not. But despite the diversity of student types who may become involved in drug use, there is, I believe, one type that is particularly prone to drug abuse. I will call such students "disaffiliates," and will summarize some of the factors that predispose these students toward drug abuse. The defining characteristic of the disaffiliate is his generalized rejection of prevalent American values, which he rejects largely on esthetic, cultural and humanistic grounds. Such students are rarely political activists, and they are rarely concerned with the issues of economic, social and political justice that agitate many of their classmates. For these students, the problem is not political or social, but esthetic: American society is ugly, trashy, cheap and commercial; it is dehumanizing; its middle-class values are seen as arbitrary, materialistic, narrow and hypocritical. Thus, those conventional values which deem experimentation with drugs— or experimentation of all kinds—illicit, are strongly rejected by disaffiliates; for them, what matters is somehow to seek a way out of the "air-conditioned nightmare" of American society.

A second characteristic of disaffiliates is a more or less intense feeling of estrangement from their own experience. Such students are highly aware of the masks, facades and defenses people erect to protect themselves; and not only do they criticize these defenses in others, but even more strongly in themselves. These feelings of estrangement are often accompanied by considerable depression and a strong sense of personal isolation. Indeed, depression following the loss of an important relationship is commonly found in the immediate background of the student who begins to abuse drugs. For the student with intensified feelings of estrangement from himself and others, drugs that promise to heighten experience seem a tempting way out of his shell.

A third relevant characteristic of disaffiliates is a fantasy of fusion and merger, which contrasts sharply with their current feelings of estrangement. In the background, many of these students have a concept of an almost mystical fusion with nature, with their own inner lives, or above all with other people—a kind of communication that requires no words, a kind of oneness with nature or the world that has characterized intense religious experience for centuries, a special kind of automatic oneness with another. For an undergraduate with an especial longing for oneness with others, the hallucinogens are especially tempting. For one characteristic of the drug experience is a weakening or breaking down of the boundaries of the self such that many individuals in fact report feelings of oneness, merger and fusion with others.

On several grounds, then, the disaffiliate is strongly attracted by drugs.

Drug use and student values

It will not do to repudiate students who misuse drugs as moral lepers and addicts without trying to understand their motives for drug use, and the values and goals they pursue. These motives are rarely simply antisocial or thrill-seeking. On the contrary, they almost always involve a legitimate (if misguided) search for ultimate meaning and contact with the world. In dealing with individual drug users, then, we must attempt to provide the student with alternate routes to attain his valid goals. Although student drug users are a small minority, they point to the inability of our society to enlist the commitments of a talented minority. If we could understand why, it might point not only to how we could "cure" drug users, but, even more important, how we might "cure" colleges and society.

As for counseling student drug users—potential and actual— I think it important to acknowledge that the question of drug use is, in the last analysis, not a medical issue, but an existential, philosophical and ethical issue. Student drug users are, as a group, extremely knowledgeable about the possible bad effects of drug use; they can usually teach their counselors, deans and advisors a good deal about the potential bad side effects of drugs. They will argue—with considerable validity—that society does not prohibit the use of other psychoactive compounds (e.g., alcohol, tobacco) which in some ways are far more dangerous than many of the hallucinogens or amphetamines. In the last analysis, then, whether one chooses or not to use drugs in full consciousness of their possible bad effects and the legal implications of drug use, becomes an existential rather than a medical decision. It is a matter of how one chooses to live one's life, how one hopes to seek experience, where and how one searches for meaning. To be sure, I doubt that we can hope to persuade students that drugs are ethically, humanly or existentially undesirable if they are not already persuaded. But I think we can at least help the student confront the fact that in using drugs he is making a statement about how he wants to live his life. And we can, perhaps, in our own lives and by our own examples, suggest that moral courage, a critical awareness of the defects of our society, a capacity for intense experience and the ability to relate genuinely to other people are not the exclusive possessions of drug users.

In the long run, those of us who are critical of student drug abuse must demonstrate to our students that there are better and more lasting ways to experience the fullness, the depth, the variety and the richness of life than that of ingesting psychoactive chemicals. Consciousness-expansion seems to me not the sole prerogative of psychoactive compounds, but of education in its fullest sense.

Thus, insofar as we can truly and honestly help our students to become educated in the fullest sense, we will be able to provide alternative routes to the pursuit of meaning, the quest for experience, and the expansion of consciousness. Obviously, much of what passes for education in America fails to accomplish any of these high objectives. As long as it continues to fail, I suspect that drugs will continue to be a problem on our campuses and in our society.

CHAPTER EIGHTEEN

Drugs: Do They Produce Open or Closed Minds?

Dana L. Farnsworth,* M.D.,
Director, University Health Services, Henry K. Oliver Professor of Hygiene,
Harvard University

A crisis of morals and values confronts this nation, and shows itself in many forms. The idealism of the young, their critical spirit, and their impatience with anything less than full justice and equal opportunity for everyone are not only admirable but a source of optimism and hope for the future. Some of their methods of expressing their impatience, however, do not always lead to a realization of their aims—they may, in fact, be self-defeating.

One of these by-products of social upheaval is the pervasive and widespread use of drugs for nonmedicinal purposes, coinciding with an overuse of many drugs which have a very important role in medicine. Under present circumstances, it is understandable that an observer would first come to the conclusion that drugs were the primary problem. Only after consider-

*Dr. Farnsworth is the author of several books on youth, health, and psychiatry, including *Mental Health in College and University,* and *Psychiatry, Education, and the Young Adult.* His life work has been student health.

This paper was delivered at the Ford Hall Forum, Boston, Mass., December 14, 1969, published in *Medical Insight,* July and August 1970, and is reproduced here with permission of the publishers.

able thought does it become apparent that the basic problem is the psychological and emotional state of those who look to drugs for a solution to their problems and thus postpone or avoid sound approaches toward their resolution. Hence, any analysis of the problem must focus on the individuals who use drugs. ". . . until an individual can understand his drug need in terms of his own psychology, drug use for him will continue to be one of the symptoms that perpetuate its causes." [1]

Almost every class entering college or high school today contains a higher percentage of students who have used illegal drugs than did the preceding one. The custom is spreading from colleges and high schools down to the junior high and even grade schools. The use of marihuana and amphetamines, especially, is escalating apparently beyond control. Thousands of young people are demonstrating lack of judgment concerning drugs. They have some realization that these are dangerous substances, yet they take drugs anyway, risking their own health, their present and future mental functioning, the legal consequences if they are detected, and the further alienation from the adult world which drug use represents. And much of this is justified by the statements that "older people just have closed minds about drugs" and "drug use makes one more open-minded."

A few definitions of these phrases are in order to enable all of us to think along similar lines.

Open-mindedness is the capacity to look at issues in an unprejudiced way, to make up one's mind on the basis of evidence that is presented, and not to hold to previous points of view in the face of new evidence. A child is basically an open-minded person, because he has no previous point of view to defend; he learns from what he sees and hears and experiences. On the other hand, the child is still in the process of learning the logic of adults. An adult would be called gullible and naive, rather than open-minded, if he believed everything he heard. To be truly open-minded, one must have some ability to use the rules of logic and reason and thus be able to judge new bits of data and discard those which obviously do not conform to the standards of logic

---

[1] J. Larner, "The College Drug Scene," *Atlantic Monthly* 216:5 (November 1965), pp. 127-134.

upon which intellectual activity is based.

Prejudice is ordinarily thought of as an unfavorable opinion or feeling formed beforehand or without knowledge, thought or reason. The word is also used to refer to unreasonable thoughts, feelings, or opinions, favorable or unfavorable, that are not subject to change when new evidence indicates that they are wrong. It is also used to indicate generally approved traits—such as prejudice in favor of honesty, beauty, truthfulness, thrift or fidelity. Here the term has changed its meaning somewhat, because it now conveys the idea that certain qualities are always to be desired over their opposites: "prejudice" usually suggests that the preconceived idea is a detrimental one. The term "closed-minded" is more or less synonymous with "prejudice," especially in the connotation of stubborn refusal to examine new facts.

True open-mindedness means that the individual is ready to listen, think, compare and contrast, and otherwise keep his mind open to new ideas—certainly always open to discarding old ideas that have become outmoded in favor of new ones that have demonstrated their usefulness. A person who insists that he is open-minded but whose opinions can always be predicted ahead of time is exhibiting just the opposite trait. A person who is so "open-minded" that he is never able to make up his mind about any question is simply indecisive. In brief, the term does not mean that one should refrain from making decisions, but rather that he should make a decision on the basis of available facts and then stick with it until there is a preponderance of evidence suggesting that the decision was incorrect.

In discussing how this relates to drugs, I should like to direct your attention to another question for a moment, and that is: Why do we consider drug abuse such a serious problem? Why is our reaction so strong and so emotional? Many of us are professional people, presumably reasonably knowledgeable about the dangers of growing up in this world but believing that we have given our children a good background and reasonable standards and that they will withstand the vicissitudes of adolescence. But we have reacted with shock, horror and disbelief when learning that our children have been using drugs. Why are we getting so distraught? What does this indicate about our capacity to be open-minded on the subject of drug abuse?

An essential first step is to realize that many persons have an immediate, emotional reaction to the word "drug." They do not see the word neutrally, as denoting any chemical substance that changes the physical or mental state of a person who takes it. Instead, they equate it with "narcotic" or "anything illegal that people smoke or inject or swallow," or "something you get from the doctor when you're sick."

In our society, the prevailing opinion is that drugs should be used only for medical purposes—to correct some condition that is causing the body to function incorrectly—and only under competent medical authority. A partial exception to this is that some drugs which do not have any great potential for danger are available without prescription, but in this case the "competent medical authority" is assumed to be the user himself. The two major exceptions to this rule are alcohol and tobacco, which our laws and social mores permit to be employed for purely social use. Other societies have at different times allowed various drugs to be used for social and religious purposes, and it is possible that in the future the use of other drugs will be permitted in our own society. But at present alcohol and tobacco are the only widely-used nonmedical drugs that are legally permissible. And the essence of the "drug problem" is that more and more people are taking various drugs without medical supervision or for nonmedical purposes.

I have said "people" rather than "young people" and added "without medical supervision," because the drug problem includes much more than young people taking drugs for nonmedical reasons. They form only a part of the problem, and their part is derivative from the main problem—the fact that we are a "pill-oriented," medicated society. Belief in the efficacy of curative drugs is part and parcel of modern medical care. Not only physical ailments, but psychological troubles also, are now being "solved" by pharmacology: tranquilizers, antidepressants, sedatives, stimulants are all available to reverse undesired moods. It is not uncommon for many Americans to use up to six mind-altering drugs each day—the caffeine in their morning coffee, nicotine in their cigarettes, diet pills, tranquilizers, alcohol, sleeping pills. There are drugs for every transient pain, every sniffle, every small bodily dysfunction. Both young people and adults are bombarded by advertising that displays the magical power of drugs. There is little necessity, they hear, for preventive measures, for endurance, for self-discipline, for more rational modes of living: any trouble that you get into, drugs can get you out of it. If your trouble is too deep for nonprescription medicine, go to your doctor, who has available the miraculous pharmacopia of modern medicine—able to prolong life, instill happiness, and cure nearly all the ills of man.

With this background, it is easy to see how today's young people grow up with the general conviction that drugs can solve anything, given the right prescription and the right dosage. The idea of changing their physical or mental state by swallowing chemical substances is thus an essential part of their cultural orientation. This is where the "drug problem" starts, in this social acceptance of drugs; it is not essentially a rejection, but rather an affirmation, of early teaching and propaganda.

Obviously, a drug used under proper medical supervision can be of inestimable, life-saving value. And probably an occasional self-prescribed aspirin or antacid does little damage. But the very complexity and potency of modern drugs has led to the complications of undesired side-effects and the proliferation of drugs to ameliorate the side-effects of others. Many physicians feel that the case for drugs has been overstated. They are a temptation to the physician: he finds it easier to prescribe a drug to clear up a symptom than to spend time and effort, and possibly frustrate the patient, in trying to discover the cause. They are a temptation to the patient: he knows he can get relief without making the radical changes that may be necessary to root out the cause of discomfort or disease. And once they are in the hands of the patient, they present a temptation to him and his friends to take the problems of diagnosis and adjustment of dosage into their own hands—to decide who needs them, and when, and how much.

Drug abuse, therefore, involves the problem of all persons who may use drugs in an improper manner. The drug abusers include physicians who prescribe dangerous drugs without full knowledge of their effects, or use a strong drug to correct a condition which would right itself in a few days, or allow a patient to take a drug indefinitely with no follow-up. They include housewives who become dependent on diet pills or tranquilizers. They include business and professional men who cannot get through the day without two martinis at lunch, or rely on amphetamines to get them through a difficult project. They include all the people who demand a broad-spectrum antibiotic every time they get a cold.

The basic effect of drugs is to change the mental atmosphere in which people live and to help them escape from some form of mental pain—unhappiness, loneliness, feelings of alienation, depression, and the inability to resolve personal or interpersonal conflicts. Marihuana, which often produces peacefulness, contentment, and euphoria, is the drug which many young people feel is the perfect antidote to mental pain. Narcotics, barbiturates and alcohol, all of which are central nervous system depressants, cause an individual to forget his troubles for the moment. Paradoxically, so do the stimulants. They may cause nervousness and paranoid reactions, but they also make the individual stimulated and self-confident, and give him a surge of energy in which he may respond actively without worrying about himself or the consequences of his actions. The stronger hallucinogens, too, may be used as an escape from mental pain, or at least as a diversion from everyday troubles.

But the desire to escape from unhappiness is not sufficient explanation for the epidemic of drug use that has erupted in the past few years. Another important aspect is that drug use, after it became established in certain key areas of life important to young people, became a symbol of the things they were trying to accomplish and the manner in which they were trying to accomplish them; peer group identification, adolescent rebellion, and the need to experiment. Because drugs have acquired this symbolic status, they have also acquired a social currency and sometimes function as a "coming-of-age" rite. Group identification and the sharing of experiences with friends are important for young people, especially in a world in which they feel cut off from everyone except their peers.

Along with rebellion and identification goes the desire to experiment. Young people are curious about unknown experiences, and they know that drugs have the capacity to produce many "different feelings." This desire to experiment is akin to other activities engaged in by adolescents and young adults, such as trying on new roles, life styles, and self-images. Often a person who is curious about drugs will try them once or twice and then stop after his curiosity has been satisfied. Even if he receives pleasure from the experience, he will decide that the manifold reasons for not taking drugs militate against further drug use.

Experimentation also involves the element of risk. This is two-fold: the risk involved in possessing and using illegal substances, and the dangers inherent in the drugs themselves. The risk-producing attributes of drugs are especially prized in that facing and conquering the challenge requires no physical exertion.

But one of the main reasons for the drug abuse problem is simply that drugs are so readily available. Once the idea of drug-taking became fashionable, a huge potential market was established, and the suppliers were quick to grasp their opportunity. This easy accessibility has meant that there is a deceptively easy answer to all the adolescent's problems right at hand. For a few dollars he can escape from his problems, defy society and author-ity, identify with his peer group, imagine he is discovering his true self, and enjoy the thrill of a dangerous and unknown experi-ence, all at once. The mystique of "drugs can do anything" is present from the medically-oriented culture; the desire to escape from personal trouble and to revolt are often omnipresent; and the dangers are seen only as an additional challenge.

Special claims have been made for the hallucinogenic drugs—LSD, marihuana (which, in the form generally available in this country, is properly classified as a mild hallucinogen), the nat-urally-occurring mind-altering substances mescaline and psilo-cybin, and various chemicals synthesized in the laboratory. These drugs are claimed by some persons to have the capacity to enlarge the scope of users' mental functions. Others claim that rather than enlarging mental functions, the drugs restrict them.

The term "expansion of consciousness" is a very indefinite one, but as nearly as I can determine, it is based on the idea that there are vast reaches of the mind which have not yet been ex-plored and which are usually not consciously functioning. Many people feel that much of what is wrong in the world today could be improved if new areas in man's mind were opened up and new goals seen and adopted. Marihuana and, especially, LSD are thought able to open up these new areas and make manifest new modes of knowledge and experience—hence the popular adjective, "psychedelic," or mind-manifesting or mind-distorting. They are supposed to aid in creativity, give access to facets of the mind that usually remain hidden, and reveal new dimensions of truth. The drugs' advocates are searching for new values: heightened esthetic response, subjectivity, introspection, self-knowledge and understanding of others, nonverbal experience, pleasure, and creativity. Drugs, they feel, are able to furnish these in a way that is quick, reliable, and reasonably safe.

One specific theory of how this is accomplished is that very early in life the mind sets up screens by which it organizes its perception. It sorts out and classifies the myriad sensory stimuli by which it is being constantly bombarded, and rejects or represses many of them so that they are never consciously perceived at all. It creates the boundaries of time and space, and the ideas of "self" and "not-self."

Some persons feel that these are artificial categories which hide and distort reality and "imprison" the mind in verbal habits and formalities. Most persons who have studied the human mind feel that they are, rather, necessary categories for a true perception of the world. At any rate, most of us think of them as basic. We live in a world of dichotomies and of cause and effect. We believe in Euclidean geometry and Aristotelian logic; we classify and sort, assign dates and labels, create clocks and calendars. We believe that the self is separate from the external world, and that our senses reveal with reasonable accuracy what is happening outside of us.

The mechanism by which the hallucinogens work is not clearly understood, but we think that their effects are mostly indirect, releasing or inhibiting particular chemicals which in turn alter the transmission of neural impulses in the brain. This does have an effect on the brain's screening and organizational processes. The senses of time and space are distorted or lost. Perception of the external world is radically changed. The most fundamental boundary of all, the sense of "self" as opposed to "not-self," the experience of being an entity separate from the rest of the world, is shaken and may be altogether broken. Depersonalization, ego dissolution, and the release of repressed material may result.

This can, in some persons, produce the feeling of being an integral part of the universe, of being in union with the rest of the world and with whatever power exists behind the world, of finally resolving all dichotomies, but it also often produces acute panic and disintegration. The psychedelic experience has been compared to religious or mystical illumination. Those who have had experience in dealing with psychotic persons also see a close connection between the unusual experiences produced by drugs and the experiences of those suffering from psychotic illness.

Mystical religious experience has been described as being "close to madness," and it would seem that this experience, however produced, can have either constructive or destructive effects in a person's life. It is so subjective that it can really be judged only in relation to what a person does with it afterwards. And when drug use is involved in an experience described as "mystical" or "illuminating," that experience usually turns out to be negative: the individual functions less well in relation both to himself and to the world outside him.

We have had no evidence that extensive use of drugs for self-realization, increased creativity, or attainment of mystical states of consciousness has been beneficial for more than a few isolated individuals. There is no doubt that many drug users are sincerely interested in achieving greater creativity; but creativity is generally regarded as including productivity. And what happens to people who become set in a pattern of drug use is that from then on nothing happens. The great philosophical theories are developed, but they are not written down; the great paintings are envisioned, but no paint is applied to canvas; everything draws to a halt.

There are distressing indications that habitual use of hallucinogens may lead, in some persons at least, to persisting delusions and to serious difficulty in perceiving the world clearly and communicating with other persons. LSD and more recently marihuana have been associated with an "amotivational syndrome"[2]; the user loses his ability to concentrate, to set and carry out realistic goals, and to communicate in the usual manner with

---

[2]W. H. McGlothlin and L. J. West, "The Marijuana Problem: An Overview," Am. Jour. Psychiat. 125:3 (September 1968), p. 128.

other persons. He becomes more and more unable to cope with reality, endure frustration, or master new material. Persons whose original orientation had been towards responsible, achievement-oriented behavior tend to change to a state of careless drifting after long-term hallucinogen use. Drug states and the supporting drug culture provide and sometimes fixate narcissistic, omnipotent defenses, and at this point adaptive effort and useful work in developing capacities may stop.[3]

The other abused drugs have the same poor record in producing any kind of real mental freedom, but they are still the hope of many persons who are not satisfied with themselves and are unable to change. Such drugs as barbiturates and alcohol may temporarily depress conflict, but they make a person less rather than more effective in dealing with his life. Tranquilizers have made life bearable for large numbers of mentally ill persons, but even those patients who respond well to them may develop an attitude of indifference towards their symptoms, their surroundings, and their personal state. Psychoactive drugs rarely increase awareness of the world; they are much more likely to contract people's lives, negate conflict, and deal with stress by dissolving it rather than by meeting it with fully human and creative awareness.

The effect of drug-taking in producing persons with closed minds is evident not just in the chemical alteration of thinking. Also of great importance is the effect which the drug experience and the identification with a drug-taking subculture has on the individual's world outlook. This includes not only his perception of the world but also his relations with other people, his responsibility to others and to himself, his commitment to values, his tolerance, his ability to understand other persons with whom he may not necessarily be in agreement.

Our experience has been that persistent drug-taking almost always has a negative effect on these qualities. The person who feels that he has discovered his own "way" in drugs very often generalizes to claim that this is the *only* way and that everybody

[3]B. W. Murphy, A. M. Leventhal and M. B. Balter, "Drug Use on the Campus: A Survey of University Health Services and Counseling Centers." *J. Am. Col. Health Assn.* 17:5 (June 1969), p. 401.

ought to follow it. With all the zeal of a new convert, he becomes a missionary of the drug culture. He urges his friends to try drugs; he engages in acrimonious debate with those who do not wish to try drugs or whose experience with them has been negative; and he associates as exclusively as possible with those who share his beliefs about drugs. Often he becomes a supplier, either because he needs the money or because he feels that making drugs more generally available is a way of solving the world's problems and an action of great value within his own ethical system.

But while he "expands his mind" and the minds of his friends, his mind becomes closed to other forms of experience. He feels that only those who have had drug experiences are fully human; he denies that anyone else's approach to life can have real value. And despite his commitment, he often suffers from deep fears that he has perhaps not found the ultimate way after all. He tends to withdraw further and further from any idea or action which might tend to demonstrate values in a nondrug experience. The fact that drugs are illegal, and that he is therefore forced to dwell more and more in a subculture outside the law and the ordinary social framework, tends to increase the feeling (often assuming proportions of paranoia or delusion) that he has found the true path to salvation.

Various sorts of narrow absolutism containing elements of paranoid thinking are not uncommon among those who have had little opportunity to examine a broad spectrum of ideas and have never learned to examine an idea dispassionately to discover what elements of value it may contain. Tolerance, an open mind, and the ability to weigh and consider are mental functions which are more acquired than innate. Much as we regret his narrowness, we can understand why a person with limited experience feels obligated to defend one idea with single-minded, blind vehemence; he knows of no other mode of thinking. But most devotees of drugs have grown up in much more pluralistic cultures, and they know how to examine new ideas, analyze another person's mode of thinking, and accept the idea that different people have different answers. At least, they did before they became involved in drugs. Drug use, first seen as a way of opening their minds to new truths, becomes instead the instrument by which their thinking is regressed and their minds closed to considering any other path of achievement.

The regulation of drug use is intimately involved with the age-old problem of the appropriate balance between the rights of the individual and the right of society to keep intact the web of morality which enables it to survive.[4] Great misunderstanding has occurred because those who stress the rights of the individual and those who stress the rights of the society have found such difficulty in understanding their own and others' premises and in communicating with each other.

The two main contentions made by the advocates of free drug use are that (a) such use is a purely private matter, not involving nor harming anyone else; (b) even if a particular drug causes harm to the user, that is his business and not society's. There would be a definite difference, in this point of view, between control of a drug that is taken quietly at home and control of a drug that causes a person to run wild in the streets and attack other people or destroy property. Considerable support would be given, even by liberals, for restriction of the second drug. It seems to me that our young people generally underestimate the danger to society that a drug-intoxicated person can be. A drug may be taken quietly at home, but if there is free access to that drug there is no control over whether it is taken in an isolated setting or whether the user, despite prior intentions, will become a public hazard. Amphetamines, for example, have caused many instances of violence. Many of the other abused drugs cause drowsiness, slowed reflexes and mental clouding. A person in this condition, driving a car or even trying to walk around in a crowded city, can be a menace to anyone around him.

Moreover, most persons have responsibilities to others—wives or husbands, children, parents, those they work with—and they are not free to do as they wish without any thought of these others. Drug use tends to reduce the responsibility of the individual and to undermine the inner discipline that directs him toward attainable and idealistic goals. In fact, hardly any action involves *only* the person who performs it—everyone lives in direct or in-

---

[4]R. C. Angell, *Free Society and Moral Crisis* (Ann Arbor: University of Michigan Press, 1958), pp. 220-232.

direct interaction with other persons and with numerous social groups. Urban crowding and economic interdependence intensify the number of such interactions and the potential for good or ill in each.

When a young person says, "The society has no right to tell me what to do in my private life," he does not take into account these fundamental facts of human interaction. The society in which he lives does, according to the philosophy generally subscribed to today, have the right to protect itself, to act in its own best interest, and to regulate the lives of its members in those areas where damage can result. Young people can see this in regard to laws designed to protect individual members of society against personal attack or loss of personal property, in laws regulating traffic and economic transactions, and in laws governing the structure of social units. They have been particularly able to see the legitimacy of the government's role in protecting and assisting the less advantaged members of the society. They must learn to see that their own acts of drug abuse can have a damaging effect on the rights of others.

Even when they have understood this, however, they are still apt to fall back on point (b); even in cases where an individual is harmed by a drug, it is his business only, not society's. In examining this claim, it will be helpful if we look also at the ideas that this point is supposed to combat:

(1) Society has the right to protect itself from loss incurred by diminished productivity of its members.

(2) Society has the right to protect an individual from harm which he may inflict on himself.

The first statement assumes the basic idea that our cultural system believes all persons to be valuable and, indeed, necessary to the society. The society is only acting for its own self-preservation when it attempts to ensure that all persons will fulfill their potential and legislates against practices such as drug abuse which tend to lessen productivity. Young people may point out that other cultures have been able to tolerate use of cannabis preparations and narcotics; they should learn that these countries have had a very real problem with lost motivation and social decay but could tolerate this because very little was expected in the first place of those persons who became drug dependent. We cannot afford to waste human resources.

Young people may argue back that they have an "inalienable right" as human beings to determine their own fate and to limit their productivity, even destroy themselves, if they wish, and that their human rights supersede the rights of the society. It is no use to argue here that we are "right" and they are "wrong," for these are questions of value which lend themselves to discussion, not to scientific proof. But we should at least be able to enter into dialogue not over "rights" and "obligations" but about the nature of the society and to what a person's "humanness" entitles him. It will help, in this case, if we remember that adolescents are often very unsure of their position in society, their goals, and their rights, and that they feel somewhat desperate about clinging to the few they do feel they possess.

One of the more difficult arguments to assess is the following: limited, self-controlled drug use gives the user a greater insight into the nature of drugs and also into himself. The person who has some personal knowledge of drugs has a breadth of experience which others do not possess, and he is not tied to second-hand evidence. And if he demonstrates the control to use a drug without its damaging him, he may thereby attain a greater open-mindedness than can the person who has never had the chance to know if he is capable of handling drugs or not.

Persons who hold this point of view question the principle that physicians, through their education and professional experience, are the only group that can be trusted to make decisions about drugs and control the supply. Obviously, not all physicians choose wisely in all cases. And it is true that other people are perhaps capable, in some instances, of making wise decisions concerning medication or drug use. But very often the best of intentions break down.

Whenever a person uses a drug and the experience is a pleasurable one, he has engraved on his mind the memory that this is an effective way of reversing a bad mood or causing a good feeling. So in the future, whenever he is exposed to pain, conflict, or fatigue (as we all are), he will be more tempted than others because he remembers the pleasant, easily acquired solution that drug-taking afforded. The more easily available drugs are, the more people will use them without a truly objective assessment of whether the long-term complications may not be more trouble-some than the original stress. The fact that physicians have such easy access to drugs has meant a disproportionately high rate of drug dependence among this group. Man is weaker than he wishes to think himself. We have never had such an array of powerful psychoactive drugs before, so we have no specific knowledge of what would happen if they were available without limitation or restriction to all who wanted them. But all our past experience indicates that the increased drug dependence would be striking, and the tragedy for society would be immense.

Both we, and the young persons with whom we are attempting to communicate, assume that the basic values involved are *freedom* and *responsibility*. Where we differ is in the means of achieving them. Young people are often inclined to think that if the other factors are working in his favor, a man is basically inclined to be responsible; but this is not always so. And often they have been unable to see the ambiguities in the idea of freedom. Freedom is not license; it is not doing anything you want; it does not include the right to interfere with other people's freedom.

Maximum freedom depends on finding those minimal restraints on individual freedom which are necessary to ensure freedom for everybody—as the Harvard Law School graduation ceremony calls them, "the wise restraints that make men free." It involves thoughtfulness, caring, being other-people-centered rather than self-centered, controlling impulsive action which may have untoward consequences. A free person must be one who has learned to predict what the consequences of his action may be. Such prediction and regard for consequences are also necessary criteria for mental health, because the person unable to carry out these functions is likely to be suffering from a character disorder which makes him unable to see the effects of his actions on other persons.

One freedom which is often overlooked is freedom of choice—the ability to use all available facts and all one's facilities in arriving at a decision. The protection of this freedom is an important function of the society. When a young person is just coming to the point where he makes basic choices about his own identity, his relationship to others, and his methods of problem-solving, it is vital that he have all his faculties and know the full range of possibilities. Drugs may destroy freedom of choice before it is ever exercised and may prevent many potentialities from ever emerging. A pattern of retreat from problem-solving and decision-making into a conflict-free world of drug use is especially dangerous when established early in life, because it cuts off all other possibilities. This is why we are especially concerned with drug abuse occurring among younger and younger groups.

There are two general points that I would like to raise, in conclusion, for your consideration. The first is that the essential task is education, of both young people and adults, concerning the reasons *for* drug-taking, rather than just the reasons *against* it, and education also concerning the effects and the dangers of drugs. Proper knowledge will have the practical effect of defusing the problem emotionally and can make possible the passage of more rational drug laws and a more wide-spread awareness that drug abuse is a symptom, not a self-defined condition. The second is that we must begin to understand what our young people are saying, the meaning behind their words and actions. We must convey to them a new sense of their being needed and of having a necessary place in this world; only if we do will we give them an incentive to face reality and accept the challenges of the modern world and of their own maturity.

People have always looked for shortcuts to efficiency and wisdom, and now that knowledge is increasing so much faster, more and more people are thinking that shortcuts such as drug use are necessary. But even if drug use does sometimes lead to increased knowledge in the sense of acquiring new raw data, it has a negative effect on the person's ability to use the data he has acquired. There is a great difference between knowledge and wisdom. Whitehead called wisdom "Common sense on a large canvas"; Karl Deutsch has said that concern without competence produces quacks, while competence without concern produces hangmen. Wisdom is not something that can be acquired by any form of wishful thinking or any form of chemical reaction within the brain cells. It can only be acquired by attainment of a rich mixture of knowledge, competence, compassion, intellectual flexibility, objectivity, and patience. Whatever else may be needed, drugs are not a part of the answer.

Index

PHOTO CREDITS

Wide World	15, 89
Bureau of Narcotics	21
North Carolina Department of Mental Health	51
Barry M. Blackman	Front cover, inside front cover, inside back cover, back cover